SEX
Academy

SEX
Academy

**ESSENTIAL LESSONS IN SEDUCTION
AND SPECTACULAR SEX**

DR PAM SPURR

First published in Great Britain in 2012 by
The Robson Press
An imprint of Biteback Publishing Ltd
Westminster Tower
3 Albert Embankment
London
SE1 7SP
Copyright © Dr Pam Spurr

ISBN 978-1-84954-250-0

10 9 8 7 6 5 4 3 2 1

A CIP catalogue record for this book is available from the
British Library.

Set in Dolly, Helvetica and Snell Roundhand

Printed and bound in Great Britain by
CPI Group (UK) Ltd, Croydon, CRO 4YY

For my husband

Contents

Acknowledgements ix

Introductory Lecture 1
Lecture Series 1:
Sexual Anatomy and Biology: Getting
to Grips with Your Body and Theirs 5
Lecture Series 2:
Sexual Chemistry: Getting to Grips with Foreplay 31
Lecture Series 3:
Advanced Sexual Chemistry: Putting
Some Fire into Your Foreplay 75
Lecture Series 4:
The Physics of Sex: Everything the Human Body Can Do 101
Lecture Series 5:
The Big 'C' Words – Confidence & Communication
Skills: How to Get What You Want 155
Lecture Series 6:
Giving an Oral Presentation 185
Lecture Series 7:
Higher Learning: Sex Techniques for Graduate Level 219
Lecture Series 8:
Ensuring Your Diploma in Sexual Achievement 265

Helpful Contact Details 309

Acknowledgements

A warm thanks to everyone who has ever shared their experiences and stories with me. I feel privileged that they have felt able to be open and honest with me about the most intimate details of their life.

I find myself again giving warm thanks to Jeremy Robson for our long-standing working relationship. Thanks also to Iain Dale for his enthusiasm and to the Robson Press team: Hollie Teague, Sam Carter, Namkwan Cho and Emma Young.

I hope that *Sex Academy* will provide lots of advice for anyone wanting to improve their sex life, though I acknowledge it doesn't specifically address the lesbian, gay, bisexual and transgender communities. I believe any unique interests of these groups are best served by specialist books sensitive to any particular needs.

Academy students will practise safe sex at all times. Condoms should be used during penetrative sex – both vaginal and anal. Relevant barrier methods (flavoured condoms, dental dams, sturdy cling film) should be used during oral sex between the giver's mouth and the receiver's genitals.

Even if you're with a committed partner you should use safer sex methods until you both have full sexually transmitted infections (STI) screenings to give you both a clean bill of sexual health or treatment options if necessary.

A word of warning: Never be pressured into having sex without condoms, etc., until you can confirm a partner's sexual history. People claim they're 'clean' when they may not be.

Introductory Lecture

Academy motto: Knowledge equals confidence and success in bed

The doors to my Sex Academy have been flung open: welcome to the most exciting lessons and lectures you'll ever attend.

Think of me as the 'Professor of Pleasure' in the study of sexual satisfaction – I aim to educate every reader to the highest standards. Nothing will be left to the imagination as everything you need to know about having the best possible sex will be fully covered in lectures. This applies equally to readers who are part of a couple or single.

The inspiration behind *Sex Academy* comes from my experience of discussing sex with thousands of people over the years in various contexts – face-to-face interviews, on television and radio programmes. As an agony aunt I've received tens of thousands of e-mails with questions about sex from A to Z – anal sex to zero sex. These conversations and e-mails have given me many insights into what makes sex fantastic for some and terrible for others.

Through all these communications a few important points strike me: 1) People forget that you should never stop learning about sex – no one knows it all. 2) Sadly too many people lose their sense of fun and humour when things get a bit tricky. 3) Despite having had lots of sex, people often understand very little about sexual desire and what makes people tick.

With these and many other points in mind I thought it was high time for a fun but informative and comprehensive guide to sex. And what better way to appeal to every willing and eager student than a specialist Academy all can attend.

What will be on the Academy's curriculum? As the Academy's Professor of Pleasure I want to ensure we cover all the subjects necessary to bring you the most satisfying sex you've ever had.

To ensure diligent study, sprinkled throughout Sex Academy lectures are Academy rules. Attention must be paid to rules and discipline is crucial for every student wanting to become the best possible lover.

Academy rule no. 1: **Pay attention in lectures as there will be relevant sex-aminations at the end of each Lecture Series.**

As with any series of lectures, we'll begin with the basics of sex that every adult needs to know – don't skip the first Lecture Series if you think you know it all, because you don't. This Lecture Series covers sexual anatomy and biology – what does what plus how your body works. It includes the all-important subject of sexual arousal and desire, and you'll discover what makes you and your bed-partner tick.

From sexual biology we move on to chemistry lectures – but this chemistry isn't boring! This chemistry is sexy and hot and includes a vast number of foreplay techniques that ensure things start and continue with a chemical reaction.

Onwards to the physics Lecture Series where you get physical with a huge range of sex positions and techniques to learn. From the easiest positions to the more sophisticated ones, each position description will include an extra tip or two to give you finesse in bed.

After the physics lectures Academy students will learn a number of communication techniques to ensure they get what they want from sex and develop their skills to find out what their partner wants. Communication techniques will be supplemented with confidence-boosting techniques.

After the Lecture Series on communication and bedroom confidence you'll receive oral tuition where the sexiest-ever oral techniques will be explained in full detail. Provision is made for techniques to satisfy both a man and a woman.

The Academy lectures now move on to Higher- and then Diploma-level sexual techniques. These will include advanced sessions on subjects like fantasy and role-play, anal sex, bondage, fetishes and other advanced sex-play.

Unlike most academies and colleges of further education, the Academy allows students to mark in this textbook. Feel free to make notes or to mark any particular techniques you want to try.

Please note that when I refer to 'your partner' throughout the Lecture Series, I mean a long-standing partner, a new partner, a one-night stand – in other words any person you're enjoying sex-play (and possibly more) with.

Finally, Academy homework will be set but it'll be fun – and sometimes feisty – so definitely give it a go.

Lecture Series 1

Sexual Anatomy and Biology: Getting to Grips with Your Body and Theirs

Welcome to your lectures on the subject of sexual anatomy and biology. You probably bought *Sex Academy* because you want some really hot sex moves and want to become the master or mistress of seduction. That's all well and good but every student should go over the basics first.

Even if you know your way around a lover's body – and you consider yourself fairly skilled in the bedroom – it's always a good idea to take a refresher course.

Lesson 1: Your bodies

Hers first: Women's bodies differ dramatically – from curvy and voluptuous to skinny and athletic. When it comes to women's erogenous zones there is also a tremendous variety of shapes and sizes in breasts, bottoms and vaginas – and all points in between.

Many women worry about the way their bodies look – particularly their feminine attributes like their breasts and vaginas. But as long as there isn't any medical/gynaecological problem, it's crucial to a women's sexual fulfilment to accept their individual differences.

Academy rule no. 2: It's time to accept your body the way it is now – and that goes for male and female students.

The basics of HER anatomy and erogenous zones

- **The pubic mound**, also known as (a.k.a.) the Mons Venus, is the fleshy area located above the vagina at hip level where pubic hair grows. It is an important zone that's highly sensitive to stimulation (more on that later in touching techniques).

- **The clitoris**, a.k.a. the 'love bud' or 'mouse's nose' (and many other nicknames), is located at the top of the vagina below the pubic mound. It is a small, slightly oval-shaped nubble containing a highly sensitive bundle of nerves that are very sensitive to touch. The clitoris swells when a woman is sexually aroused. The correct stimulation of it is crucial to by far the majority of women's orgasms.

- **The clitoral hood**, or prepuce, is best thought of as a protective cloak or hood of flesh for the highly sensitive clitoris. As a woman gets aroused the clitoral hood draws back, partly revealing the swelling clitoris.

- **The clitoral 'arms'** only became common knowledge a decade or so ago. These are located at the lower part of the clitoris and run under the fleshy pubic mound and down under the labial region. When stimulated correctly these help in a woman's arousal.

- **Labia majora** are the fleshy outer lips that run from the base of the pubic mound down to the perineum.

- **The perineum** is the flat region of skin from the base of the vagina to the anal opening. It's a highly sensitive but much neglected zone. Lots of Academy tips in the Diploma Lecture Series cover perineum and anal-play.

○ **Labia minora** are located inside the labia majora and run from the base of the clitoral hood down to the base of the vagina. In about 50 per cent of women the labia minora protrude past the labia majora.

○ **The introitus** is the name for the entrance to the vagina.

○ **The vagina** is the internal body cavity containing the vaginal 'barrel'. The length and width of the vaginal barrel varies between women, particularly during sexual arousal, when it expands, but also after an event like childbirth. During orgasm the vaginal barrel contracts a number of times giving a woman delicious 'waves' of pleasure. During intercourse the vagina is the 'receptacle' for the penis and also it obviously serves as the birth canal during labour.

○ **The G-spot** (the Grafenberg-spot) is the subject of continuing debate between sexologists with one major, recent study saying it doesn't exist and another one saying this elusive 'spot' does. For the purposes of the Academy our belief is to have fun trying to find it, whether or not it exists. Purportedly located on the front wall (stomach side), a few centimetres into the vagina, some women claim to have a spongy mass the size of a coin, which gives pleasurable sensations for them when stimulated.

○ **The U-spot** is a sensitive and small area of erectile tissue located between the urethral opening and the clitoris – most women don't realise how sensitive this area is when stimulated.

Some women enjoy being lightly touched or rubbed on this little spot (try your finger, tongue or nose!). For some it's like rubbing the genie's magic lamp. Sex research suggests that pressure on this spot might lead to a build-up of secretions in the periurethral glands inside the vagina.

And it's these secretions that might be associated with the elusive female ejaculation.

Please do be very careful stimulating this intimate and sensitive spot: too much stimulation can lead to irritation of the urethral canal – and that means cystitis. Definitely try some fantasy play to explore this area – you could pretend you're a doctor who needs to conduct a careful examination of her U-spot area. Don't worry if she doesn't find this area pleasurable – every woman is different.

◐ **The A-zone**, the anterior fornix, is a sensitive zone deeper inside the vagina – again on the front wall like the G-spot (stomach side). Some women enjoy extra stimulation in this area either with his penis or a sex toy.

Academy tip: Take the time to arouse her A-zone as sex research considers this area to be underrated. The whole area contains nerve endings easily stimulated with different sex positions and sex toys. Get your pelvic action going and try some circular hip motions as you thrust so that she enjoys stimulation of this whole upper front wall.

Further female erogenous zones

Depending on the woman, practically any area of her body, neck and head might be considered an erogenous zone. You'll hear this message repeatedly: each woman (and man) is different when it comes to their sexual response. This is very true when it comes to which areas of the body a person likes to be stimulated and finds sexually arousing – or not.

It's a lovely journey discovering your different erogenous zones from scalp to toes. Remember to take time to discover your partner's favourite zones, too. Classic zones include every point on the scalp (think how heavenly it is when your hairdresser gives you a scalp massage during a shampoo), behind and around the ears, the back and front of the neck, along the collar bone and shoulders, even the underarms and all points down the arms, inside the elbows, inside the wrists, the palms of the hands, along the fingers. Around and over the breasts (chest) and nipples, down the ribs, back and forth across the abdomen, up and down the back, around the buttocks, across the hips and obviously the genitals, the inner thighs particularly, over the knees, around the ankles, along the feet, down the toes. And all points in between!

The basics of HIS anatomy and erogenous zones

- **The pubic mound** is less fleshy than a woman's pubic mound. It is covered with pubic hair and is located above the penis. Most men enjoy being stroked on this zone as the motion pulls on the base of the penis.
- **The penis** is located at the base of the pubic mound and varies tremendously in length and girth. When engorged with blood during sexual arousal it becomes erect.
- **The foreskin**, or prepuce, varies from being very tight to very loose over his glans – a.k.a. the 'head' or 'nob' of his penis. The foreskin is retractable (it can draw back and forth over the glans, especially when non-erect) and it's there to protect the penile glans. If a man is circumcised his foreskin has been removed.
- **The glans** is located at the top of the penis and is usually a rounder, slightly bulbous shape, but this varies tremendously and it may be quite smooth and streamlined. The urethral opening is at the top of it.
- **The frenulum** is the little band of connective tissue that runs from the underside of the glans to the foreskin.

◐ **The shaft** extends from the base of the glans down to the pubic mound.

◐ **The testicles** hang below the base of the penis between the thighs. Depending on the temperature they can be loose and mobile (when warm) or tight and drawn inwards (when cold).

◐ **The perineum** is located at the back of the testicular sac and is a smooth patch of skin running to the anal opening.

Penis Fact Sheet For Academy Students

Average is not a word used frequently in the Academy as the ethos is to celebrate individuality and uniqueness. However, men wonder about penis size – often obsessing about whether they measure up – so here are a few guidelines. These are only guidelines!

◐ The so-called 'average' non-erect – or flaccid – penis is 8.5–10.5cm (3–4 inches) long from base to tip

◐ Most men are around 9.5cm (3.75 inches)

◐ The so-called 'average' erect penis is 15–18.5cm (6–7 inches) long from base to tip

◐ When erect most men's penises are 16.5cm (6.5 inches)

◐ The largest recorded flaccid penis as measured by the famous Masters and Johnson sexual research team was 14cm long (5.5 inches)

◐ The smallest recorded penis measured by the same team was 6cm (2.25 inches)

◐ *Final fact* – to date no correlation has been found between penis size and ethnic origin.

Academy rule no. 3: Erogenous zones are for exploring, so every good student should do a thorough job of it.

Are you a 'grower' or 'shower'?

The grower: when flaccid a man who is on the smaller size of average is more likely to grow a full 100 per cent as he becomes erect. So he grows a heck of a lot.

The shower: when flaccid a man who is larger than average is unlikely to grow by more than 75 per cent as he becomes erect. He's called a 'shower' because he looks comparatively large when non-erect.

Male readers please take note: the average length of a non-aroused woman's vagina is 7.5cm or about 3 inches. Once a woman is sexually aroused the average length is about 10cm or 4 inches. It's the outer 3 inches of the vagina that have more sensitivity, although some women do like their cervix (located deep inside the inward-end of the vagina) to be stimulated by a thrusting penis.

But you can take as fact that it doesn't take much penis length to fill her vagina – it's a myth that you need to be large to satisfy her!

Don't forget that if you're concerned about your penis size it'll look smaller if you have a great deal of pubic hair. There's nothing 'feminine' about trimming your pubic hair – in fact if you like getting oral sex she'll find it a lot easier than fighting her way through a great big bush. Also if you look downwards at your penis it'll appear smaller than when you look at it in a mirror straight-on.

> **Academy recommendation:** Become the 'king of foreplay' (loads of foreplay tips coming up) and pleasure her to her heart's content before you even think about penetrative sex. She won't care what size you are.

Further male erogenous zones
Students should refer to the section on further female erogenous zones above, as this also applies to men.

Academy homework: Each student must discover a new erogenous zone on their body tonight.

Lesson 2: Getting to know ... yourself
Here's a simple equation you should memorise before reading this lesson:

Knowing your own body + sharing this knowledge with your partner = satisfying sex!

With that in mind it's crucial that every student gets to grips with self-pleasure – in other words, masturbation.

It's important to dump any negative beliefs you have that masturbation is 'dirty', only for perverts, or for teenage boys – it's not. It's perfectly healthy and enjoyable and crucially gives you knowledge about what works or doesn't work in getting you sexually stimulated and satisfied.

If you don't know how your own body responds to touch and stimulation, how on earth can you communicate to a partner what works for you and what doesn't? Even more important, how on earth can you expect them to learn – or guess – what feels good to you if you don't know what feels good to you?

Turn the tables on this thought: if you're in bed with someone – whether a committed partner or a one-night stand – and they're unable to tell you what feels good, it can dent your confidence. Inside you feel insecure, that they can't trust you with how they feel and what they want.

Because of ignorance about their own body they end up embarrassed when you ask what they'd like you to do. They get tongue-tied because they feel inhibited. Basically it's a negative scenario every way you look at it.

Any negative feelings you have about self-pleasure probably came from your parents who scolded you for touching yourself when you were young. This only reflects their fears and anxieties about sex – and these are handed on down the generations. So dump your negative beliefs and take on board the fact that self-pleasure is a very good thing.

> *Academy fact:* Masturbation is only ever a negative thing if it spins out of control into chronic masturbation. In this case a person might feel compelled to masturbate even in inappropriate places like their office toilet cubicles. That's pretty darned rare and such compulsive masturbation is usually less about sex and more about relieving stress. It becomes a negative habit providing temporary relief from stress.
>
> With compulsive masturbation a person feels they don't have much power over it. Obviously a person struggles to keep this secret but inevitably it interferes with their peace of mind, relationships and/or work, and professional treatment might be necessary. Otherwise masturbation is a *healthy pursuit.*

Let your fingers do the walking all over your body as there is no wrong or right way to pleasure yourself. If you don't have experience of masturbation, choose a quiet moment when you can relax in your bedroom or bathroom. Make sure it's a time when you won't be interrupted so that you can really relax.

Do everything you'd do when with a lover – put the lights down low, put on some relaxing music and let yourself go. Allow your fingertips to touch different parts of your body.

Discover your own pleasure map

Take self-discovery and pleasure further and identify what sort of touch brings a particular erogenous zone to life. For example a woman might find gently pinching her nipples makes them spring to life, but she wouldn't use a pinching technique down her inner thighs. Instead she might find brushing her fingernails gently up and down her inner thigh gets her aroused. Finding out what sensations feel best – and where – can be shared at another time with your partner. Remember these different erogenous zones contribute towards your very own pleasure map.

If it helps you relax, imagine a fantasy scene (lessons on the pleasures of sharing your fantasies coming in Lecture Series 7). You can build sexual tension by gently and slowly running your fingertips over your pubic mound – a real teasing sensation.

Or try gently pulling on the flesh of your pubic mound – for a woman that pulling sensation stimulates the clitoral arms. If you're in the bath then definitely use the showerhead to give teasing sensations – enjoy the water trickling over your erogenous zones. As you get aroused you can gently increase the pressure to where it feels super-sexy. A word of caution: women should always point the showerhead downwards over their pubic bone – not up into the vagina – otherwise there is a very small risk of forcing an air bubble into your blood stream through the vaginal walls. It's a small risk but not one worth taking.

The perfect touch

As you know you're spoilt for choice when it comes to the wide variety of erogenous zones waiting to be stimulated. Definitely experiment with how you touch yourself: from light strokes to firmer caresses, tickling yourself a bit, 'tapping' your fingertips across your erogenous zones, even pinching and scratching (gently, mind you), massaging and swirling your way to self-bliss.

For an additional boost to self-pleasure try stroking yourself with a sex toy – either a vibrating one or a classic non-vibrating dildo. But don't stop there when it comes to added 'sextras': many women prefer to use something soft and silky like a pair of knickers to stroke themselves through rather than directly touching their clitoris/clitoral region.

Some prefer to avoid direct touch altogether and masturbate by rubbing against a cushion or pillow placed between their thighs. Other women who are highly sensitive use the palm of their hand rather than fingertips for stimulation.

The more you experiment with touching yourself the more confidence you build about knowing what you like – and more importantly what you don't like. It can also be super helpful when you touch your partner because you'll be far more creative having experimented with different touching techniques.

Academy sex suggestion: **You might find your confidence builds to such a point where you tease your partner by allowing them to watch you touch yourself. Why not turn down the lights, relax and stroke yourself while they watch – a sure-fire way to get them excited ... more on mutual masturbation in Lecture Series 7.**

Academy homework: **The men have it easier getting to know their bodies seeing as their bits are on the outside. Many women confide in me they've never even looked at themselves. Good students should 'know' their genitals, so examine your genitals thoroughly with a hand-held mirror. Appreciate the way you look and consider your genitals as being like an exotic flower. Challenge negative thinking that your genitals are ugly.**

Self-pleasure is about many things

Masturbation is not just about reaching climax and, just as when you're having full sex with a partner, so much more is going on. It's the perfect time to explore your secret fantasies, build up feelings of sexual confidence and shed any negative inhibitions that hold you back in the bedroom. It's a time you can be yourself and find out what feels good and which of your Pleasure Points are your favourite.

It's also a time to relax and spoil yourself because you can lie back, dim the lights, put on some of your favourite music and take some time. We just don't take enough time out of our busy 24/7 lifestyles.

Final lesson notes on self-pleasure

If you turned around everything you've just learned about yourself and applied it to the person you sleep with then you would be a fantastic lover. It means you want to explore their bodies fully and really understand their likes and dislikes. So treat their body like a wonderful unknown territory ripe for exploration.

Lesson 3: Arousal and desire

Time for some definitions: what's the difference between sexual arousal and sexual desire? Every Academy student should know the definitions of arousal and desire because people use these words all the time. It can be confusing and you need to filter out the conflicting information.

Key notes on sexual arousal and desire

It's fairly complex, so as the Professor of Pleasure let me simplify these definitions. Think of sexual arousal as the physical side of sex which includes all the changes that occur in your body when you're thinking about something sexy or being touched in a way that arouses you.

The most obvious example of arousal is when a man's penis is erect – his physical arousal is plain to see. But there are many changes occurring when a man is aroused and likewise there are a variety of changes in a woman when she's aroused, from the dilation of her pupils to clitoral swelling and vaginal lubrication.

Next we come to sexual desire – the mental/emotional side of sex. You know what it's like when you start feeling desire towards someone or something – you start to feel excited and tingly (that physical arousal). Desire can build to where you're quite simply desperate for sexual release.

Desire can easily be interrupted and even forgotten (think of parents about to have sex and suddenly their baby cries from its cot). When it comes to desire your brain is the biggest sex 'organ' of all. If your brain isn't excited by something, you won't feel sexual desire.

Study examples for desire and arousal

Let's take a couple of easy examples to clarify things. Think of a man who loves nice, firm breasts. If he sees a photograph of a topless woman this image stimulates his brain. The thoughts running through his mind are how gorgeous she looks – and that he desires her even if he realises he's never going to meet her. He might even get a physical response (his arousal) like a partial erection.

Or when a man gives an affectionate cuddle to his partner after a long day, think of how she might feel desire for him. These lovely, warm hugs make her feel valued and she enjoys the affection. She might not have had sex on her mind as she went to bed, but with his touch she finds her desire stimulated. As they cuddle up even closer she might start feeling physical arousal too.

I hope every student can see how desire and arousal can be part of a chain of events that influence each other and become intertwined. Remember that there are many differences between individuals and what stimulates arousal and desire in one person won't work with another. We vary tremendously and that's a good thing – the bedroom would be boring if we were all the same.

It's a fact that without desire and arousal a person won't experience sexual satisfaction, which is why so many sex researchers are interested in 'syndromes' like hypoactive sexual desire disorder (HSDD) – diminished desire. This is a big issue for many people whose desire and sexual responsiveness can be negatively affected by a variety of sources.

Academy fact: Research suggests that at any given time 40 per cent of women lack sexual desire.

A note on sex drive

Underlying your ability to get physically aroused and to feel desire is your overall sex drive. Think of this as your basic interest in sex. It's like an 'umbrella' over all your feelings, attitudes, your arousal and desire – it's your need, or drive, to fulfil these or not.

There is ongoing research around sexual drive, arousal and desire issues, but that's not what concerns the Academy. If anybody has felt their sex drive disappearing, has stopped feeling desire or has difficulty getting aroused, it's important to explore why they're experiencing these changes because not only will it affect the way they feel about themselves, it'll definitely affect their relationship.

It's not a surprise you might feel incredibly unhappy when you look at your partner – who you love – and yet don't feel any desire towards them when they try to get you interested in sex.

Sometimes your sexual interest might be there but as you caress each other you just can't get aroused. This is why so many people fake it in bed – they don't want to own up to not getting aroused. Faking it makes things even more stressful but people still do it because they don't want their partner to feel hurt.

Let's face it, it isn't a nice feeling to have your partner turn down sex – and we realise this. We don't want our partner to get a bit paranoid thinking: 'Am I a sex maniac, wanting too much?' or 'Don't they fancy me anymore?'

Or we don't want our partner blaming it on themselves for not being 'attractive enough' when that's not the case. Women are particularly bad about blaming themselves when he loses interest.

Plus people fake it because they feel embarrassed when they lack sexual desire. Men are much more likely to do this.

Academy rule no. 4: Don't fake it – it only complicates an already sensitive situation. It's far better to say that you'd like to work out why you're lacking desire and that maybe in the meantime you're happy to go along with foreplay and something like oral sex to keep your partner satisfied. Both of you should be involved in sorting it out.

Passion-killing culprits = lack of sex drive, desire and/or arousal

When you've got lots of competing feelings and possible reasons for why you aren't in the mood for sex it can be helpful to look at the main culprits. These are only the main causes and there are other possibilities plus a thousand variations on these. (Always check with your doctor or healthcare provider if you think there may be a medical reason for your lack of sexual interest.)

The checklist below applies to both men and women because although we may be different, many of the same issues affect our desire and arousal. It's helpful to separate the reasons underlying a loss of sexual energy or desire into a few broad categories. These include:

Lifestyle issues/choices
- Out-of-control stress and long working hours
- Poor quality sleep
- Drinking to excess

Academy rule no. 5: Drinking is only allowed in moderation as excessive alcohol impairs sexual functioning.

- Smoking

Academy rule no. 6: No smoking allowed during Academy homework or any sex session as smoking over a long-term period impairs arousal.

- 'Recreational' drug use
- Being overweight leading to poor circulation – good circulation is important for sexual arousal
- Excessive fatigue after childbirth and in the early months of child rearing

Relationship issues
- Arguments with your partner unrelated to sex
- Feeling neglected by your partner unrelated to sex
- Long hours that mean you have little time together

- Poor communication between you and your partner
- Erectile difficulties that mean a man avoids sex and therefore their partner feels rejected

Emotional and/or mental health issues

- Low self-esteem, low self-confidence or low sexual confidence
- Shyness and specifically sexual inhibitions
- Depression and anxiety
- Other mental health issues
- The side effects of medication taken for mental health issues

Medical issues

- Physical problems like having a bad back or other injuries
- Heart problems, blood pressure and other circulatory problems
- Diabetes and other medical problems
- The side effects of medication taken for medical problems
- The side effects of some birth control and mental health medication

Remember that although these are the main culprits for diminishing your sexual interest, very different reasons may apply to you. Most of these affect the way you feel and think – i.e., your brain action (the exception being purely medical factors, though even these can potentially upset you and affect your sex life). Research shows how powerfully our brains affect sexual desire. Put a hot, naked woman in front of a depressed man and his brain won't switch on his arousal centre. What hope has his wife of five, ten, or more, years got?

Academy rule no. 7: So all things considered it is important students don't point the finger of blame at themselves or their

partners for a lack of sex. You're in this together; you'll sort it out together.

I call all of the above 'sex stressors' – the things that stress you out when it comes to your sexual interest. Some of them are easier to solve than others. The starting point is always to identify the issue (or issues) and to work from there.

Academy homework: **If your desire isn't what it should be, spend ten minutes tonight going over the above list. Be honest with yourself and make a note of the sex stressors that might be affecting you.**

Academy sex-ample: **Let's take a lack of sexual confidence to illustrate how you might tackle a sex stressor. This is a very common issue for many people. The saying 'all mouth and no trousers' often applies to people who brag about having a great sex life but actually lack confidence in the bedroom.**

If you or your partner lack sexual confidence, try this Academy homework – it only takes a little imagination. All you have to do is 'pretend' you're someone else – either someone make-believe or a celebrity – but the person you're pretending to be must be confident and without any issues in the bedroom.

Only allow yourself to pretend for an hour. During this time you're giving yourself 'permission' to stop feeling anxious and to feel confident instead. Visualise yourself as this confident person. Imagine how it feels not to worry about how 'good' you are or not – it feels great. You can let your partner know you're doing this or do this privately in your own head.

You should find with this homework that you can let go of inhibitions for that timeframe. It can be a fantastic liberator. Do this homework regularly and you might find it has long-term payoffs for your sexual confidence.

Academy fact: Ten per cent of men can't get sexually aroused at any given time.

Hot Academy homework

It's time to apply your new knowledge – thoroughly examine the checklist and get stuck in with the main culprit. If a number of these are affecting your sex life, focus on changing one at a time.

Study example: Let's say you're having lots of arguments plus partying too much at weekends and ending up hung over. When calm, agree with each other that the arguing must stop. Then look at what starts arguments (household chores, money?) and work out solutions together.

Be the first to be affectionate and loving to your partner despite the rows. Making these efforts will have big payoffs.

Thinking of our example – arguments and partying – the next step is to knock excess drinking on the head. A hang-over on a Sunday morning doesn't lead to Sunday afternoon delight! Agree a drinks limit and help each other stick to it.

When things are better, recharge the spark. Make regular time for each other, get cosy on the settee and whisper in their ear how much you miss that 'thing' they do best in bed.

Tease them a little: let your fingertips gently run over their erogenous zones – and keep up the sexy banter. Full sex should be back on the agenda soon.

If a lack of desire continues, definitely consult your GP about ongoing health issues that may be affecting you.

Additional Academy suggestions:
If you're experiencing issues with sexual desire and arousal, check out these tips:

- Practise 'self-care' – eat well, get enough sleep and rest when needed. This gives the best starting point for your sexual desire.
- Know yourself – if you can't show your partner how to turn you on, you're not going to desire them unless they miraculously work it out for themselves!
- Turn on the flirt factor – flirting makes you both feel fab.
- Rekindle powerful feelings from when you first met – take that trip down memory lane by looking through photos from when you first met, your first holiday, your wedding if you're married, etc.
- Get the right gear – invest in a sexy garment or two that'll make you feel confident and attractive.
- Ask, ask and ask again what you can do to please your partner. By playing up your sexy side that wants to please them they'll open up more. They'll like having their very own sex god or goddess.
- Get your house in order – prioritise working hours so your energy isn't drained.
- Start exercising – by getting your heart pumping you'll improve your all-important circulation and good circulation increases sexual pleasure. Many people report that the pulsating music of a good aerobics class gets their blood pumping, leaving them more interested in sex.

The surprising sex stressors that can switch off desire, arousal and drive
I've provided you with a fairly comprehensive list of things

that are quite common when it comes to affecting your sex life. Practically anything that might seem unrelated to the bedroom can spill over into it. All of the following can leave a bad feeling in the bedroom – hopefully they'll inspire you to think creatively when trying to work out why things are going wrong:

- ❍ Little annoyances like arguing over what TV programme to watch
- ❍ Disputes over whose parents to visit at the weekend
- ❍ Annoying habits your partner has that turn you off
- ❍ Having put on weight
- ❍ Worry about the sex sounds your genitals make during sex
- ❍ Feeling uneasy about a new partner's pet that's allowed to sleep in the bedroom
- ❍ Feeling jealousy over your partner looking admiringly at a hot TV presenter
- ❍ And plenty of other things!

Let's get practical

As you'll have noticed in the homework above, very often the solutions to such things are about getting practical. Before having the 'big conversation' about why you can't be bothered to have sex always try practical solutions first. Remove the pet from the bedroom or fix the faulty lock so you don't worry about children coming in (if you have children), apologise after an argument, try and be the 'bigger person' about petty disagreements, make shopping fun by going to look for sexy gear together, promise each other to try not to let petty day-to-day issues come between you, and ask for reassurance if you're feeling unattractive.

Academy notes: when mismatched sex drives drive you crazy

As more than 50 per cent of couples experience mismatched sex drives I thought a few extra notes on this specific area would be helpful. This figure shouldn't be surprising; after all you can love someone but have very different sleep habits, have different dietary needs and simply different likes and dislikes – and the same applies to sex drive. Apart from all the things affecting drive, desire and/or arousal listed above, consider trying the following or at least becoming aware of them:

- Compromise between your different needs is always possible but understanding must come first. In an open, honest and caring way talk about how your different desires/drives ebb and flow.
- Be aware of realistic constraints when trying to compromise. If she's up for it in the mornings but he usually has early work-starts she should seduce him on weekend mornings.

Academy fact: Many men are nocturnal, i.e., their testosterone peaks at night so they feel more arousal then. Although many wake up with a 'morning tumescence', often that's more about a full bladder than feeling sexy.

- Consider the things that might stimulate desire in a partner outside of their usual morning or evening peak. With the last example in mind, she might be able to tempt her partner into morning sex-play by slipping into the shower with him. A quickie in the shower (mind you, be careful you don't slip) could be fun for both of you and he can still get to his early meetings.

◐ If one of you has your sexual peak in the evening, try tempting the other with a midnight snack of something like toast and honey. Use a spoon to dribble some of that honey down your partner's chest for nibbling and licking off in a sensual way. Or why not cut some delicious fruit slices to hand-feed them ... oops, a slice dropped down her cleavage – you must find it!

◐ When a woman has a higher sex drive in the evening she needs to think logically about trying to stimulate his interest at night – you get home from work and slip into your old, over-washed track-suit bottoms and he's definitely not going to have sex on his mind. Get back from work and slip into something sexy, light a couple of candles for dinner and things might be different.

Academy fact: **A woman's sex drive varies tremendously with the time of her monthly cycle – she may have a much higher drive when she's ovulating and a much lower one just before her period.**

◐ To find compromise, alternate having sex between your two hormonal peaks. This is realistic and it helps prevent boredom if, for example, you always have sex in the morning or always have it in the evening.

◐ Also make sure you both feel confident to initiate sex – that way you can alternate who initiates it, which helps to take the pressure off both of you.

◐ Always be understanding of and make allowances for your different levels of sex drive or different timings in your sexual interest. No one's way is the right way in these circumstances. So pointing the finger-of-blame is never helpful.

Lecture Series 1 Sex-amination

Circle the answer that you think is correct. Count up your number of A, B and C answers and then check the answer key below.

**Academy rule no. 8:** **Cheating is not tolerated in any of the sex-aminations so resist looking back over the chapter for the answers. You should absorb information as you study.**

1/ _Is there such a thing as the G-spot in women?_
   A/ _There might be_
   B/ _There isn't_
   C/ _There definitely is_

2/ _Do some men's penises grow more than others when becoming erect?_
   A/ _Yes, they are called 'growers'_
   B/ _Yes, they are called 'showers'_
   C/ _No, all men grow the same amount_

3/ _Are there different 'parts' to overall sexual interest?_
   A/ _Yes, there's drive, desire and arousal_
   B/ _Yes, there's desire and arousal_
   C/ _No, you're either horny or you're not_

4/ _What part of the male genitalia is re-tractable?_
   A/ _The foreskin or prepuce_
   B/ _The testicles_
   C/ _The shaft_

5/ _What main part or parts of the female genitalia swell(s) when aroused?_
   A/ _The clitoris and labia_

B/ The clitoris

C/ The perineum

6/ Should you give up smoking if you're having problems with sexual arousal?

A/ Yes, definitely

B/ You should cut down

C/ No, it makes no difference

7/ Can medication the doctor's given you for an illness affect your sex life?

A/ Yes, some have side effects affecting your sex life

B/ I'm not sure

C/ No, a doctor gives you medication to make you better

8/ If you're mismatched on your sex drive, what should you do?

A/ Compromise between the two of you

B/ The assertive partner should make the decisions

C/ Give up and find another partner

9/ What is self-care?

A/ It's about looking after yourself in every way

B/ It's about caring about your feelings

C/ It's about being selfish

10/ If you and your partner have had an argument what is it most likely to do?

A/ Put you out of the mood for sex

B/ Put you in the mood for 'make-up' sex

C/ Not affect your sex life

Number of As: —————————————————————————

Number of Bs: —————————————————————————

Number of Cs: —————————————————————————

☾ Mainly As: Grade A: Astoundingly hot

You're a natural. You realise that the human body is complicated and that there are many things that affect our sex lives. Keep studying like this and you'll be an astoundingly hot lover.

☾ Mainly Bs: Grade B: Could pay more attention in lectures

You didn't pay as much attention as you should. That said, you've done fairly well and just need to concentrate more in future lectures.

☾ Mainly Cs: Grade C: Needs to try harder

Oh dear, you really must try harder in lectures. I fear you won't do it but you should go back and re-read the lessons on the human body and what affects your sex life. Let's hope for better grades in the next Lecture Series!

Sexual Chemistry: Getting to Grips with Foreplay

This Lecture Series is wide-ranging, covering many areas at the heart of sexual chemistry. It'll introduce the basics of attraction, romance and flirting. It includes techniques for 'foreplay-lite' – the term I coined for the little things that can put full foreplay on the agenda.

It'll also cover an introduction to aphrodisiacs and having fun with rude-food play. The following Lecture Series covers some of the hottest, full-on foreplay techniques and more. But it's crucial that every student gets to grips with how to generate sexual chemistry. Ultimately it's one of the best ways to ensure your sex life is exciting – and stays that way.

For those of you who think you know it all, please don't skip to the next Lecture Series – a refresher course on flirting and other things to stimulate foreplay will benefit you. Everyone – even the greatest lover in the world – needs to be reminded how to set the scene for sex.

Lesson 1: Foreplay ... the beginnings

What is foreplay? Foreplay is all the fabulous fun you can have before you even have physical contact – sexy looks, flirty smiles and flirtatious behaviour, dirty phone calls, romantic messages... These are the things I call foreplay-lite – all on the flirty side of foreplay.

Then you can move on to full-on foreplay: the physical contact of touching, kissing, caressing, massaging, teasing and pleasing your lover – things that don't involve full penetrative sex but might lead to it.

Full-on foreplay includes luscious oral sex techniques and can go off the Richter scale when it comes to things like bondage. Tie your lover up and then tease them until they can't take any more sexual tension – you can't get much more full-on than that.

Open your mind to the countless possibilities of foreplay: the benefits are enormous.

Unexpected payoffs of foreplay

When you develop your foreplay skills you'll not only have far better sex, but you'll be able to enhance things that you may see as a disadvantage. Take men who fear they're on the small side when it comes to penis size. Not very many women are 'size queens' so really men shouldn't be concerned with this, but what these men should know is that mastering foreplay can make all the difference.

Becoming the king of foreplay will make you the king of the bedroom too, and you'll soon have nothing to worry about. Your partner will worship at your feet (and I'm not talking fetishes here) if you give her loads of pleasure – and even full sexual release – through fabulous foreplay.

Academy fact: Remember that foreplay doesn't have to end in full penetrative sex. You can indulge each other in lots of luscious foreplay without feeling the pressure to go all the way. Or you might decide to finish off with oral or manual sex (stimulation using your hands).

Many couples report heightened desire for each other when they indulge in a little foreplay and leave it at that. Then when they finally have full sex – later that day, that evening or even the next day – they enjoy it even more.

Additional learning: Before-play

Before we get properly stuck into foreplay you need to learn about before-play. As Professor of Pleasure, I coined this term quite a few years ago after speaking to hundreds of people about what helped begin to get them in the mood for some lustful loving.

We've already covered the many things that affect a person's sexual interest. With that in mind, before-play is all about creating the necessary vibe between you and your partner to make foreplay and sex possible. If you've just been arguing or are stressed 24/7, worried about finances, just had a baby, etc., you need to take extra care to treat each other well.

Before-play is awareness that our brains are our biggest sex organ but that they only have so much capacity. And if our 'brain space' is full to capacity with everything but loving feelings then it's hard to get in the mood.

So before-play is almost a way of life – or at least a way of taking care of your relationship. Try to 'reframe' the way you see your life with your partner (even if it's someone new in your life). Whatever your responsibilities – work, children, etc. – make regular time to love, flirt and care for each other.

Beginning with before-play gives us all the best possible chance of having a healthy sex life.

Academy homework: Prepare your foreplay pleasure chest

Every Academy student should be prepared for hot foreplay at all times. Do so by having a pleasure chest (lockable if you have children) to keep in your bedroom. It should include the following, plus anything else you want to add:

- Your favourite lubricant and massage oils. If you use condoms they should be water-based or condom-friendly lubes so as not to damage the condom. Take care not to get carried away during foreplay and get massage oils inside the vagina – this may cause irritations.
- Your favourite sex toys. (More on these in Lecture Series 4.)
- A blindfold made of soft material. It is incredibly sexy having your sense of sight taken away – it enhances all your other sensations.
- Personal grooming items like a hairbrush and comb – can be used on pubic hair too.
- Your favourite erotica to read to/with each other.
- Porn DVDs that you both enjoy.
- Sexy stockings or bondage ties for a bit of bondage play. (More on this in Lecture Series 8.)
- Body paints for playing games – paint a trail of numbers on your skin and your lover has to kiss all the way down it.
- Sexy items to enhance touching like a feather or brush.
- A rich moisturising cream to rub into your lover's skin after sex. Something like cocoa butter or coconut-based cream adds sensuality.
- Sexy surprises for your partner like a silky thong, some fun chocolates or 'love dice'.
- A sensual aromatherapy candle scented with musk or ylang-ylang.
- Condoms, dental dams and cling film for safer sex.

- ❍ A box of luxury tissues to wipe up any mess!
- ❍ Stock your fridge with erotic edibles like cream, yoghurt, jams, sauces, honey, jelly, etc. Don't forget that sticky things like jelly and honey feel fabulous on the genitals when gently warmed. Always test the temperature on your inner wrist before smoothing it over your lover's body.

All these things will maximise your foreplay – though obviously you can still have fantastic foreplay without them. Depending on your, mood foreplay can be slow and gentle or so full-on that it frightens 'the Gods' (this was said of the Hindu God Shiva, who had super lively sex-play with his consort Parvati).

Lesson 2: The science of attraction

We always assume that being attracted to someone is a purely physical event. It's quite incredible how the very first time you set eyes on someone you absorb huge amounts of information about their physical attributes – and more – in a matter of moments and without touching them. It's at this time we decide whether or not their physical self plus their non-verbal communication attracts us.

But if this first impression doesn't stimulate your desire, all is not lost. We often give someone a second chance purely because we have the time or perhaps something tells us that although they aren't the type we usually go for physically, there's 'something about them' that we like.

Attraction (and possibly desire) might grow as we absorb more details and the subtle aspects of a potential partner. We very quickly notice physical traits like height, hair colour and style, physique and the type of clothing they're wearing. But we also notice their mannerisms, how they move and the general vibe they give off, whether they look relaxed or uncomfortable.

You're unlikely to realise just how much you're picking up about someone subconsciously. But you come to a decision about whether you have any interest in them – or not – on the basis of all these things.

Your attraction radar

We can switch from feeling quite neutral about someone to being interested in them and hardly know why. For instance, if you're a man who normally goes for slim, petite brunette women and you're out with a friend for the evening, women with those physical qualities will be on your attraction radar.

While chatting with your friend, you notice a tall blonde but nothing much happens with your attraction radar. As the evening goes on part of you notices how much fun she's having with her friends, how many admiring glances she gets and, suddenly, your attraction radar switches on.

That's your subconscious noticing that this woman possesses a very attractive vibe, even if you don't normally go for tall blondes. Levels of attraction can switch from high to low because of very subtle things.

This applies equally in the other direction: if this particular man had spotted a slim, petite brunette his attraction radar would've switched on instantly. He might've kept half an eye on the situation to see if she was single. And at the same time he might've picked up that she had an annoying laugh or seemed to be grabbing all the attention. Slowly his attraction radar would've switched off again.

Once you get so far as going to bed with someone it can be a fragile balance between what turns you on and what turns you off. You can suddenly find yourself not interested in having full sex for some of the most subtle reasons – especially with a new partner.

It's a jungle out there

It goes right to the heart of our evolutionary biology to compete for someone's attention that we're attracted to. Once you decide someone is worth pursuing you start behaving in a way to get their interest and hopefully attract them. Ultimately this is down to your 'raging' genes wanting to be handed on. At the heart of your sexual behaviour is a need to reproduce offspring – even if you're a single person who doesn't want any children at this stage in your life, your 'inner' biology is still raging.

Again some of this behaviour on your part – to attract someone – is subconscious and you may not realise the sorts of signals your body language is sending out. Whether or not you get lucky depends on how responsive the other person is to receiving them.

Unfortunately you may find the person you're attracted to has a whole horde of other admirers. Perhaps they're already involved with someone, or they might miss an ex-partner and be still emotionally wrapped up in that past relationship. You may end up in competition for their attention with other admirers, a present partner or an ex-partner. It really is a jungle out there!

Some of the chemical reactions between two people

Before I get into the specifics of foreplay techniques let's think about attraction between two people. Research into love and attraction reveals that many different things attract or repel us when we meet someone. Basically we want to dive in or run a mile.

Think of it this way: have you ever wondered why a friend – who might share a lot of your same interests and attitudes – is attracted to someone you find a complete turn-off? Or maybe you spot a couple and wonder what on earth they see in each other because they just don't look like a good 'fit'? This is all because of the surprising array of things that affect attraction.

Here are some of the facts that have come out of attraction research:

◐ When we find someone attractive there are four main brain regions that become activated. Because of this activation we get butterflies in the stomach, feelings of euphoria, and so on – all the things we label 'lovesickness'.

◐ When you fall for someone a dopamine response is triggered – this is the chemical partly responsible for addiction. It stimulates a feel-good sensation. As the song says, you're quite literally 'addicted to love'. Because dopamine production leaves us feeling good it means we want to repeat this experience and see that 'feel-good' person again.

◐ Nerve growth factor [NGF] is another intoxicating chemical produced when you meet someone you're attracted to. It also causes the tell-tale palpitations, butterflies and sweaty palms. NGF production diminishes after six months, which is of course about the time the traditional honeymoon period ends – and intense sexual desire settles into something more calm. The wonderful sensations such chemicals produce get you through the early formative phase of a relationship.

◐ The amygdala, part of your brain structure, is where your first kiss literally gets implanted forever in your memory. Your first kiss is such a formative romantic event that people rarely forget it.

◐ MHC molecules (major histo-compatibility complex) are
another part of our body chemistry that give off an imper-
ceptible smell but help with subconscious attraction to
someone with a complementary immune system to yours.
This is crucial for ensuring you have strong offspring with
a wide-ranging immune system.

◐ Let's not forget pheromones – that all-important yet
largely subconscious smell that attracts us to or repels us
from another.

What much of this and other related research shows us is that we
calculate – again, largely subconsciously – how likely it is that
someone's going to be attracted to us if we're attracted to them.
We sometimes calculate for quite some time, giving someone a
second and third chance until we finally decide – often at the third
date – whether or not we want to go all the way with someone.

Not all of this happens subconsciously – you can also make
the conscious decision to boost your own attractiveness
despite your MHCs, etc. Much of this is about first creating a
comfort zone around you so that someone you find attractive
feels good in your company. Then it's about seducing them
through delicious foreplay and more.

One of the main lessons we can learn from this? Make sure
you attract someone by enhancing the likelihood they feel
good when near you.

'Signals' that attract men

You can't escape our basic biology and animal instincts when
it comes to attracting someone. And there are a number of
feminine characteristics that straight men find attractive in
a woman, highlighting to him that she's fertile and probably
able to help ensure his gene-line continues.

So, at a biological level, pert, round breasts, a slim waist-line and feminine hips signal a healthy female. Add to that 'doe' eyes set high in the face, plus pink lips and cheeks which signal youthfulness (and that's desirable to mating). Softer, slightly higher vocal tones also signal youthfulness.

Of course men vary in what they're attracted to – large breasts, small breasts, etc.; they will put in the time trying to attract the women they want to get to know.

'Signals' that attract women

In terms of our biological urges and our basic need for survival, women also respond to classic signals from a man. They pick up very quickly on the classic V shape of a man's torso – shoulders broader than hips – which is a sign of muscular strength. Research shows that during ovulation women tend to be attracted to a more masculine face – the stronger man who can protect offspring – but later in a woman's cycle, when the urge to reproduce is less, they're attracted to a slightly softer, though still manly face.

Overall women are also attracted by individual characteristics of a man – some women prefer hairy men, some prefer men with blue eyes, etc.

Your emotional make-up can attract their emotional make-up

Once two people start talking it gets complicated because quite soon we pick up messages about our emotional make-up – part of our personality that's all about relating to someone else. You might have decided that you're attracted to someone at a physical level, and thankfully in the early stages of conversation they didn't do anything to immediately repel you! But then there's the next phase, when you find out whether there's any sort of emotional connection.

Of course if you're looking for a one-night stand the emotional connection isn't important. But if you go to chat someone up thinking you might get them into bed that night for some fast sex and after a couple of drinks you just don't 'get them', you might decide not to pursue things. And that's probably down to their emotional make-up putting you off.

Do they find you attractive?

I think students will now appreciate that the initial phases of attracting someone are complicated. So how do you decide whether or not they're attracted to you?

Academy rule no. 9: Many people will be concerned about making a fool of themselves. It's always worth a try if you find someone attractive – never take a knock-back as being made to look foolish!

As over 90 per cent of communication is non-verbal – body language and facial expressions – here are some signs you can look out for.

When a woman's interested in a man
- The bridge – touches his forearm or knee gently with her hand when making a point. The bridge draws together two people's personal spaces. It also shows she wants to exclude others and have him all to herself.
- Hair flick – she flicks back her hair playfully which says, 'Look at me!' It signals a desire for his attention. Or she strokes her hair slowly while listening to him.
- The finger draw – she slowly draws her finger from her neck towards her cleavage – a signal she wants to draw his attention to her 'feminine charms' (her cleavage).

○ Hand to hip – when standing and being observed by a man she finds attractive, she gazes in his direction and unconsciously places her hand on her hip. Again, this draws his eye-line to her femininity: her shapely hips.

○ The lean – she leans inwards to him while he speaks as if she only has 'ears' for him.

○ Lingering gaze – her gaze lingers on his face while he speaks.

○ The twist – her body forms a 'twist' shape – where her upper body pivots towards him and she pivots her lower body away – which gives a flirty message.

○ The slide – she slides her fingers up and down her drink glass *slowly*. This is a highly suggestive signal suggesting she'd like to touch him.

○ Mirroring – a classic act signalling interest. She mirrors his movements in subtle ways as he speaks.

When a man's interested in a woman:

○ As above, he'll signal interest with moves including the bridge, the twist, the slide and the lean.

○ Hand to hip – when standing and being observed by a woman he finds attractive, a man will draw a woman's eye-line down towards their hips by hooking a finger in their belt loop. This is to display his man-package to her – very primal!

○ The saunter – a man will do a classic saunter or swagger when he thinks he might be observed by an interesting woman. It allows him to display his masculinity.

○ The bridge (in action) – when walking next to her he'll use the Bridge by touching either her arm or lower back to signal genuine interest.

○ Lingering looks – using lingering looks, men assess a woman's interest while also signalling their own interest.

These lingering looks help him to fine-tune his first impression – getting her to notice him if she didn't initially.

Academy strategies for foreplay-lite

You're now aware of so many elements that come into play when you're first attracted to someone and how setting the scene with someone you know through before-play is crucial. Let's take a little moment to look at some basic flirting – the foreplay-lite end of things.

You flirt because it makes someone feel good. They'll want more of your company and that includes a long-term partner. Through flirting you establish what I call your 'comfort zone' – they feel good around you, you might even make them feel special. You can do this any time, at work or with friends – a little bit of flirting smoothes over the rough edges of daily life. And a fantastic flirt knows that when they take this to the next level it makes the object of their desire more likely to be interested in sex.

Focus on them

It doesn't matter if you're flirting with your partner or if you're single and you've just met someone, the first step is to focus completely on them. Don't be distracted by your mobile – even better, switch it off. Don't look up when someone else comes in the room – instead keep your attention on them.

It's an Academy fact that the most interesting people are interested in others. For instance, if you've just met an attractive person at a party, keep it simple; ask them how they know the party-giver, etc. And if it's your long-term partner of course they want your attention!

Focus on their special qualities

The next step is to show them that you've noticed special qualities in them – this is where the clever compliment comes in. Mention something as simple as their lovely smile – said in a genuine way it'll be taken as such. Make sure you choose to compliment something that you actually like or find attractive in them.

Always keep it simple – if you think someone has beautiful hair then say just that – don't embellish with lots of adjectives which start to sound heavy-handed.

Laughter is one route to longing

As having fun is one of the main points of flirting, go for a giggle, try to make them laugh or at least keep things light-hearted. Laughter stimulates the production of beta-endorphins in the brain – these are natural opiates that help you relax. Even if you tell a joke that doesn't go down well you can laugh at yourself, giving you a 'likeable' quality.

Generate warmth

Most people are seduced by an appealing personality. Coming across sarcastic and arrogant isn't a turn-on. But coming across as caring and interested is. You can help create a sense of warmth by using a calm and soft tone of voice. Research shows the power of a warm, soft tone of voice to attract another person.

Dressing for a flirt session

We are very visual creatures; both men and women immediately notice how someone looks. Appearing too casual – and as if you don't care – isn't attractive. Putting in a bit of effort and even wearing something slinky and sexy is.

Flirting with food

Food definitely plays a part in flirting and seduction. Getting rude with food can be a real turn-on. Some foods have aphrodisiac properties and those will be described later in this Lecture Series.

Whether you're picking at tit-bits at a party while chatting with someone or sitting down to a full meal, you can try eating slowly and seductively. Never gobble down your food. Take your time and even offer to share some with them. Nothing says 'I think you're hot' like wanting to slip a spoonful of something creamy into their mouth.

Always be aware of how seductive certain foods look. Imagine an asparagus spear dripping with warm, melted butter: you slip it slightly between your lips and savour it. Guess what? Their minds will immediately wander to thoughts of oral sex with you.

Lesson 3: Some sex-tra considerations

It's crucial to think about the power of romance with a new or long-standing partner. Romance definitely heightens the possibility of sex and should be part of general before-play because it keeps that loved-up vibe simmering between you. Romance was a part of everyday life for history's great lovers like Casanova and students should never forget that their romantic gestures should be wide-ranging, including things like:

- Doing a small favour or extra tasks for a busy or stressed-out partner.
- You can never say you love a partner too often, that you fancy them or even want to get them into bed. Never take for granted that your partner knows you feel this way – they may not if you two have been super busy.

○ Compliments are always appreciated, so tell them they look gorgeous or sexy.

○ Even chores can become a bit of fun when you do something like kiss the back of their neck as you help with the washing-up.

○ Get personal and offer to do little things like trim their hair, tweeze their eyebrows and get their skin glowing with a lovely – and gentle – face scrub.

○ Never forget how fun it is to receive a surprise gift – keep it small but make it thoughtful and/or sexy.

○ Find your inner children together and do something that creates laughter between you. Snap a tea towel across their bottom as you wash up, have a little water fight as one of you climbs into the shower. Visit a park and go on the swings, go down the slide and generally lark about. These things release endorphins – those feel-good chemicals.

○ Think outside the box and blindfold them, unveil a treat like a candle-lit feast or a steamy bubble bath.

○ Get creative and have lunch or dinner in bed rather than breakfast in bed.

○ Never forget even the smallest love-note will bring a smile to them during their busy day. It can be super sexy or romantic.

○ Tell them you're thinking of them with a quick text or e-mail.

○ Show up at their office with some fresh coffee and a gorgeous cream cake – have fun sharing it.

○ Whisk them away for a quick kiss.

○ Definitely have regular candlelit dinners with some lovely mood music.

○ Concentrate on each other when you share a meal and switch off the technology. Research shows it makes all the difference to feeling loved-up.

◐ Leave them random notes in their pockets or handbag

◐ Surprise them with their favourite romantic – or erotic – DVD. Light a few candles and make it a romantic/sexy night in.

Stimulate their sexy brain chemicals

Here are some very easy but top tips to use to get their body chemistry shifting into the sex zone:

◐ Slowly drip something runny like honey or chocolate sauce on your fingers, take a little taste of it and lean over to kiss them with your sticky lips. A little bit of the lovely gooey honey or chocolate will be on your lips for them to taste.

◐ When you go to touch their hand run your fingers up the highly sensitive skin of their inner wrist. Then kiss that area and gently stroke it with your lips and tongue.

◐ Take your time to hand-feed your partner – do it sensually and slowly.

◐ As you're giving them a goodnight kiss or cuddle be a bit cheeky and run your fingers around their lips and down over their chin and neck. Little touches like that feel fantastic.

◐ If they're nibbling a chocolate or sucking a sweet lean in, kiss their lips softly and suck part of the sweetness from their mouth into yours.

◐ Your fingertips should accidentally – and innocently – brush across their nipples, thighs or stomach to give them a little thrill.

◐ Give them a sly smile then describe something sexy you'd like to do to them – be as graphic as you want.

◐ Take a breather from kissing and circle the tip of your nose around the highly sensitive skin behind their ears.

Academy rule no. 10: Students must fully accept that no two sexual partners will like the same things in bed … or on the sofa, outside, wherever.

Academy fact: Research into our natural body rhythms (called chrono-biology) shows that the best time for having sex for most people is 10pm. At that point we're most sensitive to touch. But there are wide variations and you should enjoy pleasure when you feel at your sexiest – be it morning, afternoon or night.

Lesson 4: Prepare for colossal kissing

Kissing can generate an enormous amount of sexual chemistry. It plays a crucial part in both foreplay-lite and full-on foreplay, combining the wetness of your saliva, your taste and practically endless sensuality. Never underestimate the power of a kiss – a kiss is not just a kiss because it conveys so much. For starters we 'taste' another person's biochemistry and whether they might be a suitable sexual partner for us. And it goes far past that: a super hot kiss can create huge sexual tension. Here's an equation:

sexual tension + more sexual tension = a more explosive orgasm!

Kissing is important in generating sexual tension because you're using the mouth – the all-important vessel by which we receive our life blood, food and water. We communicate with our mouths by speech and perform some of the most intimate acts with it – oral sex. Using the lips, tongue and mouth in kissing also mimics the act of full penetration during sex, so it's highly symbolic and erotic.

Academy fact: By far the majority of women complain that their partners stop kissing them after the golden honeymoon phase – with the exception of quick goodbye or hello kisses. Research confirms that the ups and downs of sexual relationships can be documented by how much kissing is going on between a couple. The more kissing, the more likely they're having sex too. Keep the pleasure going with lots of puckering up.

Whether you're a beginner or advanced kisser, do study the entire kissing lesson – you'll definitely pick up some seductive snogging suggestions.

Academy suggestions: If your partner's loving the kissing, keep it going – there's no time limit on kissing and a long kiss is very erotic.

There's nothing wrong with pausing for a moment if your mouth/tongue/lips get tired. Stop kissing and try nuzzling their face and neck gently. During this pause stroke their lips gently with the tips of your fingers – it feels heavenly.

Academy pre-kissing recommendations:

◐ Your teeth should always be clean and your breath should be fresh.

◐ Non-alcohol based mouthwashes are recommended as alcohol-based ones dehydrate the mouth leaving you prone to bad breath.

◐ Have some breath mints or disposable 'finger sheaths' impregnated with mint flavour to hand.

◐ Avoid spicy or garlicky food unless your partner is having it too.

◐ If you're with someone new give strong signals that you want to be kissed – one survey found that 56% of people think men should initiate kissing. But that means 44% think the woman should initiate kissing. So be confident and if the signals are right, who cares who begins the kiss?

🌒 When you start to kiss never lunge – move in slowly and confidently.

🌒 Soggy kisses are a no-no – make sure you don't have too much saliva in your mouth. A kiss should be moist or a bit wet – and even wetter as things get hot between you. But never start a kiss with a slobbery mouth.

🌒 Always loosen your mouth and relax your lips so they don't feel hard and 'pokey' to your partner's lips.

🌒 Keep the kissing going as long as you're both enjoying it.

Sealed with a kiss

There are many passion-inducing kissing techniques to choose from, but over the years I've found the selection below are obvious favourites. They are flexible – most you can apply to any erogenous zone not just a partner's lips. And they are sensual – they really get to the heart of what a colossal kiss is all about. Enjoy them and let your kisses travel across your partner's lips, down their neck and beyond.

You can 'show off' your sex skills to your partner during foreplay by varying the intensity of the pressure you apply with your lips as well as moving between some of the kissing types below.

Academy students should definitely experiment with these kissing techniques – you might even invent your own technique. Depending on the mood you and your partner are in, you might want to produce super gentle kissing sensations or much more passionate sensations – go with the flow.

Academy secret: Some people prefer a kiss with more 'wetness' to it than others. This brings me back to that point – never take

for granted that a new partner might like the same kissing style as your ex-partner...

Fun foreplay and more-play – kisses

Use these kisses before and during foreplay and definitely during 'more-play' – what I call that phase in sexual activity when foreplay becomes full-blown sex. That's the phase when you want more, more, more!

- **The classic French kiss** You never forget your first French kiss. That first full on 'Frenchy' is usually too wet and not erotic at all. Success hinges on relaxing your lips and opening your mouth about halfway. Start by gently probing the delicate skin inside their mouth with your tongue. As the kiss builds and your confidence grows then swirl your tongue around theirs.

- **The sliding kiss** This is actually a French kiss for beginners. Rather than 'plunging' your tongue into their mouth you slide it gently back and forth, in and out of their mouth. This warms up your confidence with a gentle start. It still feels sensual and it's the perfect kiss to use with the rude-food play – use this gentle tongue-action to slide food on to their body.

- **The Russian tease** Imagine relaxing your lips and gently swishing them back and forth against each other's lips. It sets your nerves endings to tingle mode. Your lips may even swell a tiny bit as they get teased and aroused in this unique, sensual way.

- **The vacuum kiss** This is a kiss for someone who feels confident and dominant. Relax your lips and allow them to encircle your partner's lips. Next, apply a gentle sucking action that lightly pulls on the outer rim of their lips. Pause occasionally, releasing the pressure around their lips, before reapplying the vacuum. You can also focus on either their upper or lower lip. Definitely feels sensual if you apply the suction to their lip then alternate this with lightly licking their lips with the tip of your tongue. Get creative!

❍ **The medieval necklet** A sensational kiss that begins at your lover's ear lobe and circles down around their neckline – then moves back up to their other ear lobe. As you move plant little kisses all the way along their neckline. Takes you back to the days when a knight of the realm would circle the low-cut neckline of a medieval lady's gown with such gentle kisses. For an extra hot tip use a gentle suction-action on each earlobe.

❍ **The lush lap** This is a really hot kiss that uses a lapping action. Your lips and tongue need to have some control to keep the lapping motion going across your partner's skin. Press your tongue reasonably firmly against one of their erogenous zones and using a firm lapping action you can caress that area. Between a woman's breasts is a perfect erogenous zone for this kiss.

❍ **The sloppy dog** Hugely erotic, this is the perfect kiss for using on larger erogenous zones like the neck, breasts, abdomen and inner thighs. Begin by allowing your mouth to open loosely with your tongue relaxed. Then use the action you would use if you were licking a great big ice-cream cone and apply that over your partner's erogenous zones. It's a bigger, looser tongue action than the lush lap above. This is a great technique for lapping upwards from the base of the breast to the tip of the nipple. Gently end with a flick across the nipple-tip.

❍ **The stretch** Use this kiss to gently probe the roof of their mouth, a highly sensitive but neglected erogenous zone.

Begin by French kissing and then simply stretch your tongue up to the roof of their mouth where you gently rub and flick it. This kiss can feel explosive to your partner since it's such an unusual sensation.

○ **The eastern swirl and poke** Since the first time I described this kissing technique ten years ago it's become very popular. You alternate a swirling action with your tongue with a gentle poking action. You can experiment with this during a French kiss or along their erogenous zones. As with other kisses your lips should be relaxed as you alternate the swirling and poking sensations. It's perfect to use on your lover's nipples or during oral sex across the clitoral region as long as she enjoys the sensations.

○ **The Mediterranean flick** This kiss comes from the belief that Mediterranean lovers (and perhaps lovers in other hot climates) use this technique for flicking beads of sweat from a partner's body. It's a fantastic technique for when foreplay is heating up – in the heat of passion you can gently flick (with the tip of your tongue) across your lover's lips, cheeks, neck, etc.

○ **The snake** Think of this as an advanced version of the Mediterranean flick. Loosen your tongue (of course!) allowing it to flick, lap, poke and generally imitate the action of a snake's tongue across any erogenous zone. Try it during French kissing but also on your partner's body. You can also use this kiss during rude-food play – having drizzled some yummy sauce across your lover's breasts, this is the perfect kiss to get playful with. Or try the Snake while moving up and down and around the shaft of his penis or her outer labia during oral sex.

○ **The lovers' pass** When you can seize an opportunity to turn eating into sex-play this is a fantastic technique to use. If you're eating something that you can turn into a bit of rude-food play, like a piece of chocolate, try this: pass it in a sensual way from your mouth into your partner's lips and then into their mouth. Things like chocolate, fruit or ice are perfect for doing this. Then keep being playful by using your tongue to push the chocolate around their tongue, etc.

Academy homework: Try one of the above kissing methods tonight or the next time you're with a partner.

Academy suggestion: Always let your partner know what type of kissing feels best. I can't stress enough how kissing is such an individual thing. One way of showing them which kissing technique feels best is by using this simple technique: take their fingers and suck them one at a time using the kissing sensations you love. Tell them in a sexy whisper that this is the sort of sensation you'd love to feel on your lips and even across your body.

Never forget that while kissing your partner you can keep your fingers busy. Why not stroke the tips of her nipples to start giving her sexy sensations? If you have a little bit of lubricant to hand, or massage oil, gently circle them with your fingertips. Take your time to give her loads of pleasure – alternate circling her nipples softly with a gentle pinching and squeezing. Or why not stroke the cleft of her buttocks – which is a very sensitive area – while kissing her neck?

Love-bites can be luscious
Love-bites are often seen as an adolescent thing and so end up hugely under-rated, but if you can do them with finesse they feel fantastic. Using a gentle and skilful touch they don't leave bruises. Don't use a strong sucking action in your technique;

instead avoid applying too much pressure and don't hold it for very long.

You can even miss out the neck area altogether and instead apply a gentle love-bite action anywhere on your partner's body – particularly the abdomen, inner thighs and buttocks.

Definitely alternate the love-biting with a slight nibbling sensation – obviously be very careful. Don't leave out the much-forgotten feet and toes. Some gentle love-biting on them will give your partner enormous pleasure and help release tension.

We wrongly assume the feet are off-limits except for a foot fetishist but that's simply not true. When you relax a partner's feet they relax generally and that means they're more open to your foreplay techniques. Obviously with their feet brand, spanking clean (oh dear, I'm mixing up my fetishes here!), move up and down their feet with little kisses and love-bites.

Academy technique: **Apply a love-bite sensation over the soft flesh of their pubic mound. In a woman this stimulates the deeper layers of the clitoral tissue that fans out under the flesh of her pubic bone and down into her labia.**

Academy recommendation: **Believe in yourself and all you have to offer in a relationship. Kissing can feel very intimate if you self-believe. Every Academy student should take a moment to look in a mirror. Be honest – what do you really like about your-self that your partner will appreciate? As you stand there, think through your best points in a mini-confidence boosting lecture. This is your moment to remind yourself that you can shine.**

The beginnings of foreplay techniques

Foreplay techniques are wide-ranging and I can't stress that enough. Seeing as you've just improved your knowledge of kissing, why not try something different like brushing your partner's teeth? Suggest it playfully – give them a smooch – then say you want to clean them and use small, circular brushing strokes on each one.

They'll love it as you treat each of their teeth like a precious pearl and this gentle technique is a lovely intimate thing to do together.

Lesson 5: Let's get rude with food foreplay

Having covered some kissing techniques, let's explore foods fit for foreplay. Taste is an incredibly powerful sense and when you stimulate it with aphrodisiac-type foods they heighten your pleasure. People vary when it comes to taste preferences, but the foods I include are noted for the fun you can have with them – and/or for their aphrodisiac properties.

Academy suggestions: Here are some foreplay tips for 'supper-time' seduction:

- ❍ Wherever you're eating – kitchen, dining area or in a 'lust nest' you've created in your bedroom or sitting room, use a dimmer switch or candles for subtle lighting. It creates a seductive vibe and remember, when you play down one sense (in this case with more subtle lighting) you automatically heighten other senses.
- ❍ Many people have hang-ups about the way they eat so practise eating confidently – even sexily – in front of a mirror.
- ❍ Have lovely, soft napkins and finger bowls ready because hopefully you'll end up hand-feeding each other.
- ❍ To create more intimacy share one plate or platter of food rather than having two separate plates.

- The same applies if you're mixing up a delicious cocktail – share one large cocktail glass with two straws to sip from.
- Don't forget the mood music – as the saying goes, 'music is the food of love'.
- Hand-feeding each other tit-bits of food will hopefully lead to other things.

How to hand-feed your partner to make it part of foreplay

You can have such fun with food. To boost your confidence – and make it a sexy eating experience – try these tips:

- If possible always use small bite-size pieces.
- Use a small spoon rather than a big dessert spoon when spoon-feeding your lover something like ice-cream or creamy chocolate mousse. Especially if they're a new partner they might feel self-conscious opening their mouth wide enough for you to get a large spoon in.
- Even if using a small spoon or fork, keep the morsels of food small.
- Where appropriate run the edge of the food around their lips before placing in their mouths – a sexy technique for something like a juicy asparagus spear or slice of fruit.
- Break things like a delicious slice of cake into small pieces to hand-feed.
- Keep a soft napkin ready to wipe the corner of their mouth.
- Definitely kiss any crumbs off their lips.
- Test the temperature of heated foods, like a chocolate fondue, on the inside of your wrist before placing into their mouth, e.g. a marshmallow or strawberry dipped in warm chocolate.
- Grab their attention when eating something with your fingers, like asparagus, and linger with your lips gently sucking the tip of it. They'll get the message.

◐ Let your hair down and get messy with your rude-food feast.

Having tried some food-based foreplay, stretch out and become your partner's 'dessert'. Lie in a comfortable warm place on a big soft towel (for easy washing). Let them dribble a few cake crumbs over you or smear anything smooth and creamy on to you. They can gently kiss and lick these little morsels off you. If he likes something sweet he can turn her into an ice-cream sundae. She lies on the bed with a towel underneath her bottom. He parts her legs and spoons a little ice-cream (don't worry, she'll soon be warmed up with his tongue!), chocolate sauce and whipped cream over her labia. He slowly laps at it, teasing her as he goes.

Tasty and sexy treats

Put to good use the foods you most love. For instance, if she has a taste for French pastries buy a fresh cream éclair, split it open and wrap it around his penis. She can carefully nibble it off him very slowly – I don't know who'll enjoy it more, him or her! He'll get more turned on when her lips and tongue make their way through the éclair and he can feel them on his shaft.

Or find a new use for a ring doughnut: she eases it on to his semi-erect penis and takes little bites of the sugary doughnut. The perfect way to clean up after some rude-food play is to share a steamy shower.

A little bit of aphrodisiac history: There's a long and rich history of foods being used as aphrodisiacs. The ancient Mexican emperor Montezuma supposedly drank fifty cups daily of pure chocolate laced with hot chili to fuel his exploits with his 600-strong harem. The great lover Casanova apparently gave chocolate love charms to the women he wanted to seduce. And the revered and beautiful

Egyptian empress Cleopatra was reputed to drink a mixture of ground almonds, spices, honey and yoghurt, believing it to be an energising aphrodisiac.

Along with aphrodisiac foods I've included other classic 'aphrodisiacs' below. A word of caution here: don't get carried away believing that an aphrodisiac will be a sure-fire fix for a flagging sex life – it won't. Some aphrodisiacs, like horny goat weed, have a little research supporting their energising properties. However, others might only have a placebo or psychological effect (you think it's going to make you feel sexy, so then it appears to work).

Academy warning: **If you're taking any medication definitely check with your doctor before taking an aphrodisiac preparation, many of which are available over the counter at health food shops or on the internet. Never be over-keen and take more than the recommended dose of preparations like Yohimbine, which can cause nausea and vomiting – not sexy. Also never buy aphrodisiacs from internet companies unless they're a company you know and trust – only buy from reputable health food stores. If pregnant don't take any aphrodisiac compounds, except of course those listed below like nuts and fruits.**

- ◐ Almonds – Contain properties said to revive flagging desire. Traditionally a symbol of love and fertility in Mediterranean cultures, almonds are baked into savouries, sweets and desserts.
- ◐ Asparagus – Greens are good for you. Asparagus is rich in vitamin E which is necessary to keep your bits in working order. And hand-feeding your lover an asparagus spear dripping with warm butter is a sensual experience.

◑ Avocado – These are loaded with essential fatty acids and anti-oxidants that help the production of sex hormones. Their smooth and creamy texture is very sensuous. The Aztecs called the avocado tree the 'tree with testicles'.

◑ Avena Sativa (green oats) – Sometimes this is mixed into preparations with other aphrodisiacs because it seems to boost their effects. Research seems to support the view that it boosts libido, particularly in people with low testosterone. Usually found in extract form, it may be added to food and drinks.

◑ Bananas – As well as being great for your health, bananas are said to have energy-giving properties. They're ideal to share baked with honey, cinnamon and hot cream. Try spoon-feeding each other. For best effect, bake them in their skins as it's actually an alkaloid in their skin that has an 'aphrodisiac' effect. This is released by the baking process.

◑ Chocolate – Chocolate is rich in energy-boosting chemicals – the darker the variety the better. It contains the chemical phenylethylamine which stimulates the brain giving a euphoric effect. It usually contains caffeine too so potentially it provides an energy boost and enhances your mood. Something very simple like feeding your lover strawberries dipped in warm chocolate can raise the temperature between you.

◑ Damania – Having a botanical name that speaks of lust (Turnera diffusa aphrodisiaca) is one of the most popular aphrodisiacs. Grown in hot countries, Mexican women serve hot drinks containing damania before lovemaking as it's said to create a mild euphoria. The presence of several alkaloids in it boosts circulation, thus aiding sexual arousal. It's sold in capsule form or as a tincture to be taken a couple hours before lovemaking commences.

● Epimedium grandiflorum – Historically the use of this as a sexual enhancer dates back two thousand years to China. The plants are pulverised and then sold in capsule form. As with any capsules bought from health food stores, you can take them as advised or break them open and mix them into cooking.

● Figs – These look gorgeous and sexy but they're also full of vitamins. The ancient Greeks supposedly indulged in orgies once the fig harvest was complete.

● Ginger, cinnamon and ginseng powder – For two thousand years the Chinese have used ginger as a stimulant and other eastern cultures do the same with cinnamon. These can be used in baking or sprinkled into dressings.

● Ginkgo biloba – Taken from trees found in Japan and China, this is known to increase blood and oxygen flow. It is also said to enhance mood and have a knock-on effect on love-making. It is very popular in the USA, where it's now grown. You can buy capsules containing this combined with other stimulant herbs like ginseng.

● Horny goat weed – A herb that was traditionally seen as a sex remedy for men has now been marketed for women, too. There are various energy drinks containing this.

● Lavender oil – Renowned for its relaxing qualities, the scent is also said to stimulate sexual interest. Put a few drops in your bath (unless pregnant, in which case you should not use aromatherapy oils) or sprinkle some on your sheets and pillows.

● Maca – This plant is grown at high altitude in South America and is believed to give energy and vitality.

● Muira Puama – Found in the roots and bark of an Amazonian tree, this is particularly popular in Germany. Available in its raw form, you can brew with it and add it to your favourite drink. It's also available in capsule form and may be mixed in with other aphrodisiacs. You can also get it in so-called potency patches.

◐ Orgasm 'creams' – There are various creams that you can rub onto your genitals which supposedly increase sexual arousal and blood flow to the genitals. Many of them work with mild skin irritants like menthol-type products. These simply irritate the skin giving a sensation some find pleasant – and others find quite irritating! Some contain L-Arginine, which is an amino acid known to increase blood flow to the genitals for about ten to thirty minutes on each application. Always purchase from a reputable source and follow instructions carefully. Zestra is an oil available in sachets which is applied directly to your genitals and contains natural oils that boost blood flow and stimulates nerves.

◐ Oysters and other seafood – Oysters contain high levels of zinc, which is beneficial to health and energy levels. Research has found they also contain two chemicals: NMDA (N-methyl-D-aspartate) and D-aspartic acid that help release both testosterone and oestrogen. But any seafood is fairly seductive simply through presentation and taste.

◐ Padma 28 – This herbal extract from Tibet has undergone clinical trials which found it was effective in improving blood flow to constricted arteries. Enhancing blood flow is important to achieve arousal.

◐ Pollen extract – You can purchase a food supplement, Femal, containing a pollen extract which purportedly relieves irritable moods and supposedly boosts libido.

◐ Pumpkin seeds – These are known for their beneficial effects for prostate health in men and production of testosterone. Packed with zinc, they are now seen as beneficial for women too.

- Rye – Not particularly sexy but rich in energy-giving minerals that might help sexual performance.

- Scents – Essential oils can play a part in setting the scene. Cleopatra (again) used rose-scented carpets to seduce Mark Antony. Ancient Egyptians used many other fragrances in baths and oils including cinnamon, jasmine, patchouli, musk and frankincense. The Romans scented every part of their beds, walls and baths. The Greeks were known to use floral and wine-scented oils on their bodies to heighten their sensuality. As long as you don't have sensitive skin you can add a few drops of most essential oils into a bath. Alternatively you can burn candles scented with these oils.

- Sesame seeds – These are packed with vitamins and minerals which are energy-giving and thought to help with fertility.

- Testosterone creams – These come in different strengths (male and female) and are rubbed into the skin. Some people find surprising results.

- Vanilla – Has been popular in love potions for centuries. It tastes and smells delicious and is ideal in scented candles and oils. It's a fantastic flavouring for a rich dessert to savour with your partner.

- Ylang-ylang – As well as its beautiful scent it is an essential oil renowned for its euphoric and mildly relaxing qualities.

- Yohimbine – Evidently better at increasing male libido, yohimbine is a commonly used aphrodisiac in Africa and the West Indies. Scientific trials on rodents and humans have shown a positive effect from this product derived from yohimbe tree bark. It boosts neurotransmitter levels and can be brewed from its natural form into a tea or taken as a tincture, available from some health food stores.

Here are some other foods which potentially increase energy, boost circulation and/or help libido: swordfish, lobster, crab, salmon and other oily fish, liver, onions, garlic, wheat germ, pumpernickel, sunflower seeds, sweet potatoes, yams, squashes, turkey, mangoes, papayas, blueberries, other dark berries, wheat grass, pomegranate, kelp and other seaweed, and sushi just because it looks sexy.

Academy warning: There are many supposed 'aphrodisiacs' to avoid. Unscrupulous people will play on sexual insecurities to make some quick money. Scientists have poured scorn on various animal-based aphrodisiacs. For instance, in Oriental cultures there is a great belief that eating the penises of animals will give you their strength. However, the tissue found in those parts of an animal is not much different from tissue in the rest of its body. Never buy in to claims that potions based on items like rhino horn will enhance your libido. These simply aren't based on fact and something like rhino horn has about as much aphrodisiac effect as chewing your own fingernails. Plus buying such things only promotes illegal hunting of such animals.

Then there is the infamous Spanish fly that's made from ground-up Cantharis beetle. It should definitely be avoided as it may be downright harmful. Rather than making you feel sexy it irritates the urinary track giving you an 'itch' down below. And evidently it can be fatal for some people eating it!

Academy fact: Indulge in some sexy aphrodisiac-style desserts containing chocolate, bananas and vanilla before you burn off some calories with the following positions: the Doggy position will burn 180 calories. 'Women on top' positions will burn off 140 calories and in the Lovers' Knot you'll burn 170 calories (all positions described in Lecture Series 4).

Some yummy things to share with your partner that aren't necessarily aphrodisiacs:

- ◑ Anything creamy like ice-cream or your favourite flavours of fruit yoghurt.
- ◑ Anything sticky like honey, chocolate, marshmallow, toffee sauces and jams.
- ◑ Desserts like éclairs, mousses, petit fours, cream cakes, etc.
- ◑ Any type of fruit like grapes, mango, papaya, apple and peach slices.
- ◑ Anything you can hold with your fingers – mini cocktail sausages, hors d'oeuvres, olives (mind the pits), smoked salmon and other finger sandwiches, sticky Oriental mini-ribs, etc.
- ◑ Finger-sized vegetable crudités dipped in luscious dips.
- ◑ Many types of Japanese food are fantastic for hand-feeding. If you don't like raw fish you can buy sushi made of vegetables.
- ◑ Even chips can be seductive if you trade off feeding each other.

Extra Academy tips for getting rude with food

As the list above shows, it's easy to turn everyday foods into some flirty fun. Get adventurous and your rude-food play might lead to full sex.

Honey heaven

- ◑ Honey is fantastic to use in foreplay because it's so sticky and lovely – and it's good for you too. Why not keep a pot handy by your bedside to dip into during foreplay. A little honey tip – if you lick your finger before you dip it in the honey then it'll come off your finger more easily as you swish it across your lover's nipples or lips. Without 'licking and then dipping' you risk it sticking to your finger as much as it does to their erogenous zones.

◗ So you thought 'tea and toast' was innocent? Surprise your partner with tea and toast in bed, including some luscious golden honey to smear on the toast ... and each other!

Belly-button bliss

The belly button is a much-neglected little erogenous zone. Because of this it's actually sensitive to even the gentlest touch. When you're sipping your favourite liqueur try this tip: as you sip from your liqueur glass stroke your partner's stomach and then move to their belly button. Circle it lightly with your index finger. Suggest they lie back and then pour a little liqueur into their belly button. This can be gently lapped out– you'll be surprised by their physical response.

Because of the belly button's location just above their pubic zone, you also increase sensitivity here as you stimulate it. So why not rub your fingers gently back and forth over their pubic zone as you lap against the edges of their belly button, heightening their pleasure. Just make sure their belly button is clean before you do this – maybe best done after sharing a sexy shower or bath together.

Seductive strawberries

An extra little trick is to turn some ripe strawberries into sex-play. After dipping them in warm chocolate have your partner lie back so you can swirl the chocolate around her nipples. Obviously make sure – as with any warm food-play – the chocolate is only warm and not hot. Then enjoy licking the warm chocolate off her nipples before sharing the strawberry with her.

Memorable melon

Not only does juicy tropical melon look sexy and erotic, it can also be turned into a seductive dessert or brought to bed on a platter to play with. Take some ripe, sweet melon chunks and trace them around her nipples. As little droplets of juice splash across her breasts you can lick up every little drop. Then when the melon is finished you can continue caressing her breasts with your tongue and lips.

Naughty Nyotaimori nights

This is a Japanese speciality where paying customers feast off of glamorous women reclining with food beautifully placed around their bodies. Have fun re-creating this in your home. Choose some favourite foods that can be placed across your/ your partner's naked – or sexily clad – body. Tasty little cakes and nibbles are perfect to use. You can lie down on soft blankets in your candle-lit sitting room or bedroom – obviously you should be warm and feeling confident. After spreading a light feast across your body, you call your partner when you're ready. This should be fun/pleasurable and not stressful.

Delicious dessert

This is a scaled-down version of Nyotaimori nights; a simple tip requiring a little yummy chocolate and his desire to give some tongue action. Break off a square or two of chocolate during foreplay. Then slide them on to her pubic mound and continue foreplay, using your fingertips to make sweeping circles of this area.

Next he can go down between her legs and with his fingertips move the melting chocolate to between her lips – the labia lips! He gently pushes the warm chocolate inwards with his tongue and continues licking. As it melts he can enjoy the melting chocolate mixed with her juices and she'll love the sexy sensations she gets. Think of the rock 'n' roll myth that Mick Jagger did this with a whole Mars Bar – not quite so subtle.

Wanton whipped cream

We all know that whipped cream is naughty but nice and also creamy and sensuous. You can now buy good-quality spray-can whipped cream to use so you don't have to whip it yourself. Keep it handy for foreplay. Get artistic and once she's got her top off carefully spray some whipped cream around her breasts. The coolness will make her all tingly – use your fingertips to swirl it around her breasts and down her abdomen. Then you can have fun lapping it off with your tongue. Don't forget you can move on down and spray some on her pubic mound and labia to kick-off oral pleasure!

Home, sexy home

Never forget the importance of scent in creating a warm foreplay vibe. If your partner has a favourite scent then get creative, for example, if they love cinnamon place a cinnamon stick on a baking tray in a low oven. In a short time their favourite scent will be wafting around. The same goes with chocolate – microwave some pieces and then leave them out for their scent to spread. Or prepare some hot chocolate and leave it on the table near your settee so that area is filled with chocolatey smells. Scented candles are incredibly popular for this very reason – if someone has a favourite scent they can create it anytime they want to.

The food of fetishes – sexy splodging

Splodging is the fetish some people have for playing with and rolling in cream cakes and buns and any gooey foods. Splodgers organise events where like-minded people roll about in all sorts of creamy, sticky and rude foods. Most people would find it too messy, but you could have fun every so often for a special occasion. Try some 'mini-splodging' and protect your bedding by putting some old (but clean) sheets or towels on top of your regular ones. Then let go for a good old food fight with some cream cakes to splodge on each other and roll around in. Definitely a good way to shed any inhibitions.

A final word on rude food

People don't have enough fun in the bedroom and can get anxious about all sorts of things – most of the time sex should just be fun and not too serious. Definitely enjoy some 'frolics' and fun with rude food. Be a little creative and do things like serving up little 'nipple cakes' for dessert – these are little iced fairy cakes topped with a glacé cherry in the centre. Or cut a banana in half, fill it with cream and pop a little cherry on the end for your homemade penis-lookalike desserts. Or just arrange sensuous-looking cakes on a platter for an evening of fun. There are many specialist bakers that will supply sexy-looking desserts for special occasions.

Academy technique: simple erotic pleasures (SEPs)

This is an important concept every student should memorise. There are so many little things you can do to kick-start foreplay and further sexual activity, BUT these are also great to do just for their own sake because they're simple and they're pleasurable. These are SEPs – simple erotic pleasures. Feeding each other rude foods, as above, is an excellent example of an SEP.

SEPs help strengthen the intimacy between you both. For instance, have you ever tried shampooing your partner's hair? Try this in a loving and gentle way – massage their scalp tenderly and they'll get a lovely warm feeling inside.

Or offer to brush their hair – and do it gently. Or moisturise their body when they come out of the shower using sweeping motions over their body. Why not towel them dry with a warm soft towel? Why not paint her toenails and fingernails? Take each finger separately and gently hold them; painting the nail is very sensual.

SEPs are all about being playful and tender in unusual ways. They help stimulate little nerve endings – like on her fingertips – that usually get neglected. I highly recommend using SEPs whether you're with a new partner or in a long-established relationship. They are particularly good if you're dealing with a sex stressor mentioned in the last Lecture Series – you may not want to have sex but you'll want to have SEPs.

SEPs help you think outside of the usual 'box' when it comes to foreplay. They can stimulate interest in trying something new. And definitely help you keep all-important physical affection going, especially when you're not actually having sex due to an issue in your life.

They can be incredibly important to making sure you don't feel distant from your partner or help you re-establish an intimate bond. They let your partner know you care about them no matter what's going on in your lives. SEPs can be spontaneous and often only take a few moments (like brushing your partner's hair or towelling them dry) but can make all the difference to your relationship.

Academy rule no. 11: Enjoy SEPs any time – and every day if possible – with your partner.

Lecture Series 2 Sex-amination
Circle the answer that you think is correct. Count up your number of A, B and C answers and then check the answer key below.

1/ Are there any particular techniques to hand-feeding your partner?
   A/ Just be careful not to give large portions
   B/ Yes, there are lots of little tips to make it sexy and pleasurable
   C/ Don't have dirty hands

2/ What is the 'sloppy dog'?
   A/ It's a sex position
   B/ It's a type of kiss
   C/ It's food – a type of hot dog

3/ Can you use body language to show attraction to someone?
   A/ It's confusing but I think you can
   B/ Yes, definitely
   C/ No, you have to use spoken language

4/ What are SEPs?
   A/ Some easy pleasures
   B/ Simple erotic pleasures
   C/ Some easy positions

5/ What do almonds, chocolate and ginger have in common?
   A/ They're tasty
   B/ They're all aphrodisiacs
   C/ You can eat them

6/ Why is flirting important?
   A/ It boosts your confidence
   B/ Because it makes you – and someone you're attracted to – feel good
   C/ It might get you laid

7/ What happens in the eastern swirl and poke kiss?
   A/ You use your tongue in different ways.

B/ You swirl your tongue and then poke with it to give two very different sensations

C/ You make sure you don't poke their ear when you're kissing their neck.

8/ What is splodging?

A/ It's something to do with food.

B/ It's an activity some people find exciting involving getting messy with mainly wet and moist food items.

C/ It's the mess left when someone decorates their house with paint.

9/ What is flirting-lite?

A/ It's when you don't want to have sex.

B/ It's very gentle and subtle ways of showing interest to someone.

C/ It's something that helps you diet.

10/ What kind of erogenous zone is the belly button?

A/ It's only an erogenous zone when it's kept clean.

B/ It's a much-neglected erogenous zone.

C/ It's not an erogenous zone.

Number of As: _____

Number of Bs: _____

Number of Cs: _____

◑ Mainly As: Acceptable ... just about

There is room for improvement but if you promise to pay extra attention you can move on to advanced sexual chemistry.

◑ Mainly Bs: Better than hot

Well done, you paid attention in lessons and you're well equipped to move on to advanced sexual chemistry.

◐ **Mainly Cs: Complete concentration required**

You've obviously been day-dreaming in lessons and you might find it harder to attract someone having failed this Lecture Series.

Advanced Sexual Chemistry: Putting Some Fire into Your Foreplay

Now you're ready for lessons to further develop your foreplay techniques. This Lecture Series covers a variety of touching techniques and then familiarises you with some super hot techniques to try.

Lesson 1: Top tips for getting tactile

The brush of skin against skin is electrifying and helps build sexual tension. Unless you're apart and cyber or phone sex is your foreplay, you're going to be touching your partner from the beginning of foreplay through to full penetration. Always remember that while you touch you can continue sexy banter and flirting – a lesson on talking dirty coming up.

> *Academy fact:* The sense of touch is the very first sense that's stimulated when we're born. Coming through the birth canal and then being handled with loving care post-birth is a bonding experience that super-activates this sense.

The skin is packed with touch receptors and nerve endings. As we go through life these are stimulated, first within our family when we get cuddles and later when we have relationships from (usually) mid- to late adolescence onwards. Sadly for some, as they grow older they have less tactile stimulation – obviously they stop getting cuddles from their parents but if they don't end up in relationships this particular sense becomes under-stimulated.

Of course you can reawaken the wonderful feelings you get from touch at any point. But be aware that the next person who comes into your life may like a different level of affection and touch than you do, depending on their experiences. You can always encourage more affection and touching with the tips below and make your foreplay irresistible.

Academy suggestion: Take a moment simply to think about the most sensitive and least sensitive areas of your body. For instance, your fingertips are far more sensitive than the backs of your hands. And places that aren't normally stroked or touched, like the backs of your knees or inside your wrists, are also highly sensitive. An area like the inner thigh is far more sensitive than the outer thigh, for example. But it's these very different levels of intensity and sensitivity to touch that makes exploring a partner's body exciting. Remember to guide your partner to these.

Generally women have nearly twice as many nerve endings in their skin than men, which is why women often want more foreplay – it feels fabulous and they can't get enough. Despite this, most men still enjoy lots of touching. Or they find they want more touching once they've been touched!

If your skin has gone into hibernation you can re-stimulate it with these tips – equally good for men and women:

◐ Invest in a good body brush and regularly brush your skin in long sweeping motions. This exfoliates your skin but also helps to sensitise it.

◐ Take a hairbrush (preferably with natural bristles) and gently brush your fingers and palms of your hands. Use little circular motions to bring jaded skin back to life on your hands – so important to foreplay.

◐ Alternatively, if you don't like body-brushing invest in a good exfoliating scrub. There are many body scrubs aimed at women but also for men. Use the scrub while in the bath or shower with gentle rubbing in circular motions around your skin. Take time to scrub your whole body – your skin will tingle all over.

◐ Try waxing – for women the legs, bikini line and underarms, and for men the chest, 'back, sack and crack'! It'll leave your skin feeling wonderful and ready for loads of foreplay.

◐ Run a warm bath and throw in some luscious scented bath oil or bubbles. Then get in with a cup of ice and run one piece at a time around different parts of your body while sitting in warm water. As one piece melts take another and run it along another part of your body. Both men and women should try this. Circle your nipples and down towards your abdomen, up and down your inner thighs, carry on over your shoulders, around your knees, behind your knees, and even around your genitals. It's invigorating and exciting for your skin.

Top touching tips

Here's a quick study list to prepare you for touching your partner during foreplay:

◐ Rub your hands together to warm them up before touching your partner.

◐ Keep checking with them if the sensations feel pleasurable.

◐ Always have the confidence to say if something doesn't feel good or has stopped feeling good. They'll want to know!

◐ Keep your nails trimmed and hands as soft as possible. Rough skin and calluses don't feel sexy moving over a partner's skin.

◐ A warning to men – don't forget how your facial hair might feel to her. Particularly when it comes to oral sex, most women want a smooth and shaved chin. But you need to be aware of this at any point during foreplay when your face may brush against any part of her.

Academy suggestion: Whether you're in the early stages of your relationship or you've been together a while, ask your partner to lie back for some sex-ploration. Make sure they're warm and comfortable and tell them you want to play a little game exploring their 'pleasure map'. Suggest they rate the different ways you touch them between one and ten (with ten being the hottest).

Get the touching started

Students are just plain wrong if they think there's only one or two ways to touch someone. There are many different ways to use touch and any of them can be used with or without massage oils or lubricants.

For starters, always remember to vary the pressure of, for example, a circular motion with your fingertips. You can begin with extremely light circular moves around your lover's nipples, increasing the pressure with your fingertips as you move down their body to their pubic bone.

Remember that when you're touching highly sensitive erogenous zones like the pubic bone and clitoral region, it's not just the specific area you're touching that gets stimulated.

There's also 'secondary stimulation' from the nerve connections that run right through our bodies. So if you gently rub her pubic bone she'll probably get sensations deep in her vagina.

Academy touching techniques to give loads of pleasure

Basic stroking

Keeping your index and middle fingers together – in a relaxed way – use them to move in an upward stroke. Try little stroking movements followed by larger ones. Use the basic stroke anywhere from stimulating large areas – like the upper back – to much smaller areas like the sensitive area where the inner thighs meet the outer labia.

Rubbing

Think of this as a smaller and subtler version of stroking. You can visualise it like a 'sanding' motion where your index and middle fingers rub gently back and forth in very small movements. Definitely try this on small erogenous zones like behind the ear, behind the knee, at the top of the cleft of the buttocks and on different parts of the genitals. This is a really hot technique when you add a touch of massage oil or lubricant.

Drumming

Alternate drumming with your index and middle fingers to create a lot of sexual tension and a hot sensation. Think of drumming as gentle raindrops falling on the skin. Your partner can lie back while you gently tease them by drumming across any erogenous zones, particularly trying it across their pubic bone or around the base of his shaft or down her labia.

Fluttering

This builds on the drumming sensation but uses all of your fingertips. Flutter your fingertips across your partner's neck, breasts, abdomen, buttocks, inside their thighs, around their knees – anywhere you think a gentle fluttering will feel good.

Twirling

Perfect for super delicate places. Imagine you are very gently twirling a pen between your thumb and index finger. It's incredibly stimulating when you gently pull on your lover's skin and twirl back and forth – again I can't stress how gently. If she can take direct clitoral contact she'll probably love this twirling sensation on her clitoris or her clitoral hood. He may enjoy the sensation at the base of his testicular sack where the skin is loose.

Circular massage

Apply a simple small circular massage movement with your index, middle and ring fingers (held loosely together in a relaxed way) across any erogenous zone. This is a fab technique for increasing the blood flow to erogenous zones, enhancing sensations.

Listen to what your partner says and if they particularly love one technique then give them loads of that. But never overdo touching one area – it can end up over-stimulated, particularly if it's the clitoris. So if, for example, she loves you drumming around her clitoral region, you can always pause and move down between her thighs for some sensual stroking before going back to the drumming.

The whole experience of touching

When you think about touching as part of foreplay you can also think about it as a complete experience. Think about the feel of your bedding. If your sheets are starched and stiff, or old and ragged, they won't feel sexy against your, and your lover's, skin. Try and keep them smooth and soft. Some people go all the way and use silk or satin bedding for extra softness.

It's the same for things like pillows and cushions on your sofa – if you're going to have fun in your sitting room they shouldn't be tatty. Early in a relationship, when you're quite experimental, you might want to keep a soft blanket or throw in the kitchen cupboard just in case you get carried away on the counters or table if you get frisky.

> *Academy motto:* Always be prepared! Be ready to throw a comfortable and soft blanket on to something hard like the kitchen table if you're likely to have a quickie. The same is true for foreplay and sex 'alfresco' (outside) where you both need to be comfortable with a soft blanket below you and/or on top of you for warmth.
>
> When you use your ingenuity like this and have everything ready for a day out, alfresco sex can become a fait accompli: preparation makes these things more likely.

Foreplay fitness

Research repeatedly shows that the more physically fit you are the higher your sex drive will be – plus you have the added benefit of better orgasms. Generally keep your fitness in mind and, as mentioned in the first Lecture Series, the more things you do that are bad for your health, the less fit and the less interested in sex you'll be.

Fitness can be fun and even sexy if you do something like take a dance class together. At the very least you can take romantic walks together which give you time to chat and stay connected.

And have fun working out together – buy a home workout DVD and do it together but dressed in sexy work-out gear.

Keeping flexible is fantastic for your health and sex life. Flexibility means you're more likely to try new sex positions. Even doing five minutes of simple stretching or yoga-type exercises daily will enhance your flexibility.

Luscious lubes

Definitely get the lubricants out during foreplay. Remember your good bedroom manners and warm the lube up between your hands before rubbing it into your lover's erogenous zones. Use lubricants for all the above techniques like tapping and drumming lightly, stroking and gentle pinching.

Men love loads of lube when you're using some of the stimulating hand techniques below. With loads of lube between your two hands experiment with different movements – carefully, mind you! I've got lots of hand techniques coming up so pay attention.

Pump up the volume

To heighten your foreplay, think about the music you have on. American research found that hard rock music actually gets your blood pumping and heart racing. Since these physiological signals mimic sexual arousal it can help intensify your foreplay experience. To help get you both in the mood think about your choice of music.

Lesson 2: Advanced touching techniques

Once you've mastered these straightforward techniques you can build your repertoire to include some even hotter and more sophisticated things. It's easy to get a bit anxious about trying something new on a partner, but it comes back to that same old saying – *all you have to do is ask* if they like the new touching techniques. And never take it personally if they don't like something you've tried – sex-perimentation doesn't always get perfect results. The point is to have fun learning what works. Just keep on asking as you explore foreplay techniques so you know your partner's OK with what you're doing.

Here are a few sexy foreplay techniques using different types of touch to get started with:

The 'V' sign technique – a guaranteed victory!

I've never known a woman who didn't get turned on with this technique. It'll stimulate her clitoris without direct touch. Make sure you've given her lots of foreplay first – don't just dive straight down to her clitoris.

Move your middle and index fingers into the traditional 'V'-for-victory sign. You can relax your other fingers and thumb outwards from them. Begin by moving these two fingers back and forth over her pubic mound below her belly button. Then turn and angle them so your index and middle fingers slip down towards her pubic bone so they're either side of her clitoris.

Now the pad of your index finger and the pad of your middle finger each rest on one of her outer labium. Begin rocking your hand gently so your V-sign strokes up and down her two labium. This action softly stimulates her clitoris by pulling gently on her outer labia, which then pull on her clitoral 'arms'.

Remember her clitoris is the little 'bud' visible underneath her clitoral hood. And the clitoral arms are connected through tissue below her clitoris running under the skin including into the labia, which is why the V-sign action stimulates her clitoris.

Labial massage

After some sex-play have her lie back with her legs relaxed.
Make her comfortable and then using your thumb and fingers
gently massage her labia as if you were gently kneading bread
or cake dough. Begin at the bottom of one of her labium – near
her perineum and move your fingers upwards massaging her
labium and taking as much time as she wants.

> **Academy rule no.** *12:* I can't stress how gentle you should be
> when massaging her labia or clitoral regions to heighten her
> pleasure. Only build pressure when she asks you to.

As your fingers massage up towards her clitoris pause and
gently circle it. Then continue and move back down her other
labium. Definitely use your favourite lubricant so your fingers
can slip along gently as they massage.

The full four

Allow all four of your fingers to relax and move down, slipping
over her pubic bone. Your fingertips should now gently touch
the entrance of her vagina – the introitus. Begin with a delicate
touch as all four fingers stroke, rub or circle with massaging movements around this area. Take note as she gets more
aroused and lubricated and then you can allow one or more of
your fingers to slip inside her vagina.

Alternating hands

Use this technique on any larger area like the breasts, the
buttocks, the inner thighs, etc. Be generous with lubricant or
massage oil and place your hands on the area to be massaged,
e.g. the inner thigh. While one hand pushes downwards the
other hand pulls upwards, gently alternating back and forth.

You can imagine how your hands pass each other as they alternate their up-and-down movements.

For added pleasure when massaging the inner thigh make sure your finger nearest your partner's genitals gently skims this area to tease them.

The erotic 8

This is a whole body massage technique to try while your partner is lying on their back. It feels fantastic and stimulates large areas of their body. Definitely use lots of body massage oil. Begin with your hands together at the centre of their breastbone swirling outwards so your hands part and move under their breasts or side of their ribcage (if you're doing this on a man). Then bring your hands back together at the point just above their belly button.

Next swirl your hands back outwards along their hips and then bring your hands back together at their pubic bone. Now you can see how your hands are moving in and out, creating a figure-of-eight shape. Now you repeat the swirling of your hands back up their body – your hands coming together just above their navel, then outwards and back up to the top of their breastbone.

You can repeat the whole figure-of-eight sequence as many times as you want. Try varying the pressure and the speed that you use to swirl in and out over their body. Have them turn over on their stomach as it also feels heavenly done on the back and buttocks as they lie on their stomach.

A *sex-tra tip*: as you do the erotic 8, for extra pleasure bend over and plant little kisses along the trail your hands make.

Using touching techniques in other ways

During foreplay you can use any of the touching techniques

above in different ways. For instance, when touching inside her vagina you can use the drumming technique, etc. Of course your timing's important and she should be well lubricated when you start fingering inside her.

Five top Academy tips

1/ Take it slowly with penetrative techniques. Let's say you're caressing her inner thighs and start running your fingers over her labia – you could start giving her a labial massage. Next you could slip one finger just inside the entrance to her vagina and gently move it around. Then withdraw it and continue stimulating her labia. She'll probably be super excited by this teasing so it's the perfect time to ask if she wants you to re-insert your finger(/s).

2/ Always make sure that you get feedback from her on how it feels when you're running your fingers over her labia and into her vagina.

3/ Never start penetrative touch with more than one finger – until she's ready two or three may cause her discomfort or even pain.

4/ Keep lashings of lubricant coming to ensure she keeps moist.

5/ Don't forget to tell her how sexy you find slipping your fingers in and out of her – she'll get more excitement knowing you find her 'bits' beautiful.

Hot Academy touching tip: Definitely try 'the stir' on her for an amazing penetration technique. Slowly insert your index and middle fingers together into her moist vagina. Take your time and slowly and sensually move them inside her as if you're making a 'stirring' action with them. Think of it as if you're stirring a luscious bowl of something creamy. Keep this

**gentle action going as you stir them around and around, stimu-
lating the entire inside of her vaginal walls.**

Some 'forbidden' touching

Increasingly people are exploring anal sex. This is a very
individual thing: some find it a big turn-on and extremely
pleasurable while others would never want to try it.

**Academy rule no. 13: Having a bit of anal pleasure or full anal
sex is a personal decision and no one should EVER feel pressured to have anal foreplay or sex.**

If you and your partner are interested in exploring it, here are
some key tips to help make it a pleasurable experience during
foreplay. Information on full anal sex will come in Lecture
Series 8.

- ☾ Make sure you're both in a relaxed mood for anal foreplay.
  It won't be pleasurable if that area is tense. Begin sex-
  perimenting with some gentle touching of the perineum
  and anal area. A reminder: the perineum is located on both
  men and women running upward from the anal passage to
  the opening at the base of the vagina on a woman, and up to
  the testicular sack on a man.
- ☾ Even if you're not having full anal sex (though after the step-
  by-step guide in Lecture Series 8 you might change your mind)
  you must use safer sex practices. Use some sort of barrier
  method for fingering the anal area like slipping your finger
  into a condom or latex glove (available from a chemist).
- ☾ When it comes to oral stimulation of the anal area use a
  dental dam or sturdy cling film to prevent transmission of
  bacteria from the anal area to the mouth.

● As the anal passage doesn't lubricate itself the way the vagina does you'll need lashings of condom/latex-friendly lubricant even for fingering only. Please keep re-lubricating the area.

● Anal foreplay can involve gentle fingering or 'rimming' – where you use your tongue and lips to stimulate this area through a dental dam or cling film. This area is highly sensitive so you can stroke, gently massage, kiss and generally play around. Simply begin with some gentle caresses. You can follow these with circular movements with your fingertips. And then as your partner relaxes you can insert your fingertip.

● Beware you don't over-stimulate the anus as it can get quite sore.

In the last Lecture Series I mentioned simple erotic pleasures (SEPs): now that you're ready to step up the action here are a few more suggestions:

Scalp massage

Your partner will love some heavenly hair-play. A scalp massage feels amazing – your partner can lie back with their head in your lap or you can stand behind their chair with their head relaxing back. Begin by gently stroking from the top of their forehead back along their scalp to the base of the neck. Repeat this a few times. Now place your fingertips at the top of their forehead again, but using a gentle pressure start circling your fingertips instead of stroking back over their scalp. Slowly move over their scalp to the base of their neck, pausing while you circle your fingertips for a bit before moving your hands back a couple centimetres to restart circling again.

Brushing their hair

If you've never experienced it, it feels fabulous when someone brushes your hair – an SEP some will sadly never experience. Begin by standing over your partner and, starting from the forehead and working backwards, brush their hair rhythmically with long, sweeping, gentle strokes. Your partner's going to love you for this pampering!

Washing their hair

Another SEP some of us never experience (unless we get our hair shampooed at the hairdresser). Have your partner sit in a warm bath while you shampoo them. Be creative and glide the shampoo around and around their hair. Rinse with lovely warm water. Then wrap them up in a warm towel as you gently and carefully comb out their wet hair.

Oriental hair massage

Time for something a bit sexy – why not tease and tantalise your lover's skin with your own hair? Have them lie comfortably while you straddle them. Wearing something sexy while doing this adds to the sensuality. Bend over them as you gently swish your hair across their nipples, down their abdomen, over their genitals and anywhere you think they'll like. Even a man (or woman with short hair) can do this SEP as the ends of short hair can feel just as nice stimulating the skin as long, swishing hair.

Turning up the heat

The Thai body massage is a really hot foreplay technique – you both may not be able to resist full sex after this. The Thai body massage gets its name because Thai masseuses would use skin-on-skin contact during a massage with a client to arouse them in the hopes they'd pay for 'extras'. For a really sensual experience kneel over your partner and gently skim your naked chest/breasts across theirs. Move back and forth slightly before you start skimming your lower pelvis against theirs.

How to make it super hot: she can brush her labia sexily against the edge of his penis – or he can swish his erect or even semi-erect penis across her nipples, tummy, thighs and genitals. Take turns as the partner on top doing the 'swishing' and also have your partner turn on their stomach so you can do these moves across their back and bum.

This type of skin-on-skin contact is a huge turn-on and it creates a strong bond of intimacy.

Increasing sexual tension

There are many other ways you can create sexual tension and heighten your partner's foreplay experience.

Sexy materials

Foreplay doesn't just have to involve your hands, so get creative and add in new sensations. For example, touch her through her silk knickers. This can feel fantastic, especially if he uses his fingertips in little up and down movements along her labia with the silk between his fingers and her genitals. It increases sexual tension because she knows there's very little between his touch and her most sensitive erogenous zone.

Or take the satin sash from a dressing-gown, moving it up and down and around your lover's genitals. Done gently and sensuously it can be a hot part of foreplay.

Feathering

This is one of the most popular foreplay techniques I've recommended over the years. Take a feather (clean, obviously!), available from an adult shop or even a crafts store, and use it with some massage oil. Have your partner lie back while you squirt some oil over their skin. Then take the feather and gently use the tip to trace circular, back and forth, or squiggle patterns through the oil over their skin, from their nipples to their genitals. It's incredibly sensual and really cranks up the tension.

There's a place for talking dirty in foreplay

There's lots coming up on talking dirty in Lecture Series 5, but don't forget to sprinkle your foreplay with a little bit of dirty talk to create an earthy mood. But for extra sexy fun you can use a commanding tone of voice as you ask her to, for example, 'open your legs further' so you can stroke her inner thighs.

Academy rule no. 14: Students should never blurt out anything really raunchy with a new partner – you might completely put them off sex with you.

Ice can be nice

Using what's to hand can create fun foreplay. Let's say you're sipping an icy cold drink – take an ice cube between your lips and trace a line around your lover's nipples and down to their navel. These areas are highly responsive to the cold. You can then kiss and lick them to warm them up or use your fingertips to move the ice around their body.

Get creative with ice-play and freeze some sliced ripe strawberries. Once frozen you can run them over her lips, neck, nipples, and all the way down her abdomen. As you go lick the luscious droplets of juice from the melting berry slices.

Luscious liquids

Again, don't miss a trick when you are sharing a drink with

your partner. If you're celebrating an occasion and you're sipping some champagne/cava, why not trickle a little into your partner's waiting lips. Or take a sip of your cocktail, lean over and kiss them, trickling a little into their mouth. You can trickle a few drops down their chest to gently lick off. Or get a bit naughty and have them lie back and part their legs. Now you can trickle some exotic-tasting drink onto them and gently lap it off. Full oral techniques to come in Lecture Series 6.

The swan technique

Use this technique on him; it gives a lovely subtle stimulation for his penis and testicles after you've explored his other erogenous zones. Form the swan by bringing together your thumb and fingers in the shape of a swan's head. Begin by clasping his testicles gently between the 'beak-like' shape formed by your fingers. Using a subtle, gentle circular motion give them a little pull.

Next relax your fingertips and swirl them up the shaft of his penis and then back down around his inner thighs. Then re-apply the 'swan' as an upward movement starting at the base of his penis, pulling his foreskin (if he has one) *gently* up over his glans – the head of his penis.

If he's circumcised gently flutter your fingertips up and down the shaft of his penis. Next you can clasp the base of his shaft and gently and rhythmically move your hand up and down. Bear in mind what he wants – pulling upwards only if he wants that stimulation. Circumcised men vary tremendously – some have much less sensitivity, requiring more stimulation, and others are highly sensitive.

Double hander

The double hander is great to use on her breasts when she's lying on her back. It's easy to do if you're kneeling above her and unbuttoning her shirt: you can gently scoop either side of one of her breasts between each hand and sensuously move your hands upwards to her nipple.

Focus on one breast at a time and check if she wants you to massage more deeply with the double-hander scooping movement. If you're giving her a full body massage then the 'double hander' feels fantastic on each bum cheek when she's lying on her stomach. It gives an incredibly relaxing and erotic sensation because people hold such tension in their buttocks.

Try the double hander on him when giving him a back massage. Move down to his buttocks and take each one separately – with each hand either side of a buttock – and move upwards to join your fingertips together.

Blind man in the buff

Get daring and heighten the pleasure you give each other during foreplay by taking turns being blindfolded – a quick way to turn up the heat. Use a comfortable blindfold (widely available in adult shops, or improvise with something soft and silky like the sash from a dressing gown). By eliminating sight you heighten your enjoyment of touching sensations.

Make sure your partner feels secure when blindfolded (it can be quite daunting for the first time), is comfortable with subtle lighting and decides whether they are partially clothed or naked. Personally, as your Professor of Pleasure, I think keeping some sexy knickers on makes this more exciting!

When you're both comfortable the blindfolded person should just relax and enjoy the sensations as you touch them. Use fingertips, your lips, your tongue or even a well-lubricated vibrator to run over their skin. Ask what feels best and then withhold it for a few moments to really tease them.

Hot Academy suggestion: make your partner guess what you're touching them with – is it your tongue, your lips, your fingertips covered in lubricant or the lubricated end of a vibrator?

Voyeurism for two

Kick-start some lusty feelings between each other by visiting a high-quality pole-dancing club – if you both feel happy about it. Many couples enjoy watching the show and it can put you in the mood for some sizzling sex when you get home. Don't be too shy to try out some private dancing at home – stripping tips coming in Lecture Series 7.

The Roman bath – foreplay fun in the bath

It's so sexy sharing a shower or bath together, so why not try this playful technique. Get in the bath together with one of you seated behind the other. They're the one 'in charge' – pretend they're the Roman emperor or empress. They get to reach around and caress and fondle their partner with the lovely bubbly water around them.

Try trickling warm water down your partner's back while kissing and nuzzling their neck – so easy to do since you're sitting behind them. You can take it to the next level with a bit of sexy chat pretending they're the Roman sex slave.

If you don't have a bath, stand behind them in the shower and do the same nuzzling and fondling. You can also do this when sitting on the floor innocently watching television – your partner between your legs with their back to you. Use your tongue and lips to gently stimulate behind their ears. Have the TV remote handy because you're sure to turn it off!

As your arms circle around her caress and touch her breasts. Cup and massage them and then run your fingers down to between her legs – still from behind. While sitting in front she can wiggle and grind against his crotch to stimulate him. This is an easy way of starting sex-play when you're doing something ordinary like sharing a bath or watching telly.

Morning glory

Teasing your partner in the morning with some foreplay but *without* satisfying them is definitely the way to explosive evening sex. Pet them and stroke them while in bed, rub them down with a warm towel as they get out of the shower and give them a big passionate kiss as you go out the door. You'll both be thinking of it all day.

This is a good technique for varying the time that you have sex, especially for people that always have sex in the morning – that can get a bit stale. And if you always have sex last thing at night definitely have some fun sex talk about what you'd like to try in the morning. In this case the rule is to talk but don't touch until you wake up.

Tease their toes

In the first Lecture Series you learned about the variety of erogenous zones – few are as sensitive as the toes, which we've touched upon briefly. You're missing out on some hot sensations if you've never received and given a foot/toe massage. Make sure you're both comfortable with it and your feet are clean and scrubbed. Use a lubricant or massage oil on your hands and begin by gently caressing their feet with an upward movement from the ball of their feet up to their toes.

Check what feels good as if it gets too ticklish it doesn't feel erotic. After using the upward motion towards the tip of their toes you can try gentle circular movements with both of your thumbs on the bottom of their feet. Continue giving feel-good

sensations by circling the ends of their toes individually with
your fingertips.

If they're freshly showered (as they should be) you can
follow the fingertip massage by trailing little kisses down
their ankles to the tip of their toes. If you two are having a
leisurely foreplay session then crank up the heat by placing
a succulent grape between each toe – and then nibble them
slowly one at a time.

Slipping off your clothes without it looking like a sitcom

It's no wonder people get anxious about undressing in front of
a partner – most of us aren't very coordinated and don't want
to make a hash of it. During foreplay this can feel challenging
when you get to the point that clothes should be coming off.

To avoid having any comic moments where you're stuck
trying to get something off or trip trying to slip out of trousers, here's a few Academy pointers:

For starters, take your time – there's no rule saying you
have to get your clothes off quickly.

Ask for help – in a sensuous voice ask your partner to help
with your zip, etc. This can turn into part of the foreplay. It
can be fun as they help undress you.

Once you're in your underwear you still don't need to rush
to get naked. Explore each other's erogenous zones while
still partly dressed. He can play with her bra strap, flicking it sensuously. Or pull down the front of a bra, exposing
her breasts to kiss her nipples. Or run your fingers under
the edge of her lacy underwear to give her some lovely
sensations.

She can also playfully touch and tease him through the
pants or boxers he's wearing. Enjoy these moments particularly if you're not planning to have full sex.

Naughty nicknames

Lots on talking dirty coming up in Lecture Series 5, but for now don't forget that during foreplay you should give each other hot and sexy nicknames. Start with some classics first like 'big boy' and 'sexy chick', but as you get more confident and things get raunchier turn up the hot factor on the pet names you give each other.

There's never a final word on foreplay

I can't give you the final word on foreplay because there are endless possibilities for what you might do. Foreplay can start slowly, then you might pause and then it can end up in quickie sex. It's whatever you make of it – start from flirting, have fun with it, get super sexy, heighten desire and sexual tension, and finally fully satisfy with it.

Touch is terribly important to foreplay – when we stroke, caress and stimulate each other's bodies we release the bonding hormone oxytocin. This heightens our experience of touch specifically and foreplay generally.

The key thing is to 'get lost in the moment' during foreplay and enjoy it for what it is. Let your hands, lips, tongue, legs and full body move against and tease your partner. You can touch them and move with them until you and/or your partner can't take any more sexual tension.

Lecture Series 3 Sex-amination:

Circle the answer that you think is correct. Count up your number of A, B and C answers and then check the answer key below.

1/ *The point of foreplay is?*
   A/ *To give each other pleasure even though it might not lead to full sex*

    B/ To get someone to have sex with you

    C/ To make your partner feel good

2/ Can music be part of foreplay and sex?

    A/ The right music can help turn you on by getting your heart pumping

    B/ No, because partners have different musical tastes

    C/ It might help set the mood

3/ What is a Thai body massage?

    A/ It's where you give a massage with your body

    B/ It's a massage you have in Thailand

    C/ It's where one of you gives the other a special massage

4/ Would ice ever have a part to play in foreplay?

    A/ Yes, if you were careful how you used it

    B/ No, can't see that working

    C/ I'd be wary of trying that kind of foreplay

5/ Do men have twice as many nerve endings in their skin as women?

    A/ No, women do

    B/ Yes, men are bigger so they must do

    C/ No, I think it's equal

6/ Can anal sex ever be just a bit of foreplay?

    A/ Yes, it can

    B/ No, it's full sex

    C/ Maybe

7/ Is the Roman Bath a foreplay technique?

    A/ Yes, it is but it's so hot it might lead to full sex

B/ No, it's having a bath in Rome

C/ I think it might be

8/ Approximately how many different finger techniques are there for foreplay?

A/ There are loads

B/ One or two

C/ About four or five

9/ Can foreplay be used as a way of stalling full sex?

A/ Yes, definitely

B/ No, it speeds up getting to full sex

C/ I'm not sure

10/ Is it a good idea to give each other sexy nicknames during foreplay?

A/ Yes, if you're tactful

B/ Yes, the raunchier the better

C/ Yes, if you can get up the nerve

Number of As: _____

Number of Bs: _____

Number of Cs:

☾ Mainly As: Astoundingly hot

You'll go far with your foreplay. You understand that it can be fun and playful, and also ranges from simple and flirty to super hot and dirty.

☾ Mainly Bs: Best re-read the whole chapter

You're just not thinking when it comes to foreplay. Resist making quick decisions - instead think things through. Otherwise re-read this Lecture Series.

◗ Mainly Cs: Could pay more attention in lectures

You're maybe a touch unsure about foreplay techniques. Build your confidence so you realise that it can be whatever you and the person you're with want it to be.

The Physics of Sex: Everything the Human Body Can Do

This Lecture Series will help you discover the laws of physics – or at least of getting physical with each other in the most pleasurable ways.

Key lessons range from learning the very best sex positions to having fun with a whole host of sex toys, all accompanied with unique sex tips and techniques to enhance a number of these positions.

Lesson 1: Strengthening your sexy PC muscles

First let's begin with something every student should know. To give both men and women more powerful orgasms and enhance his staying power you should exercise your pubococcygeous muscle (PC) every day. This muscle runs from the pubic bone down through the perineum up towards the bottom in both men and women.

Identify it by squeezing the muscles you would squeeze to stop yourself urinating and those that control your bottom – those are the PC muscles. Begin by working them out gently, squeezing for two to three seconds for ten repetitions. Build to twenty repetitions, twice daily, for the rest of your life.

PC muscle repetitions can be done sitting, standing or lying down and no one will know you're doing them. They're fantastic for women during pregnancy and after childbirth to recover or maintain their pre-birth vaginal strength.

The Johnny-come-lately technique – As your PC muscles get stronger you'll find your orgasms get more powerful for both sexes, and for men the extra PC muscle strength helps them last longer during penetration. The Johnny-come-lately technique is where they squeeze their PC muscles as they get nearer to climax – this squeezing action slows him down so he can then continue thrusting. This can be repeated as many times as he wants during penetration so he can last and last.

Academy homework: Men should definitely try my special 'Dr Pam's tea-towel test' to gain super-strength. Drape a tea-towel (or face cloth or hand towel) over your erection or semi-erection and bounce it up and down to gain more erectile strength.

Women can gain extra PC strength in various ways. She can begin by grasping hold of a vibrator or dildo and pulsate her vaginal muscles around it. She can buy an Oriental love egg or beads as described in the sex toys lesson below and learn to walk around holding them in, exercising both her PC and vaginal muscles.

Academy suggestion: Give each other a hot thrill during penetration by pulsating your PC muscles. This isn't just to slow him down but to give both of you really sexy sensations.

Academy rule no. 15: All students will work out their PC muscles so they can have stronger climaxes and last longer.

Lesson 2: Condom confidence

A reminder about safer sex: you must find out your partner's sexual history if you've decided you'd rather use other methods of birth control and intend to give up condoms. Giving up condoms means you should both get full sexual health screens.

If you're not prepared to do that and are going to continue with condoms it's crucial to develop condom confidence – a phrase I coined many years ago. This simply means developing the confidence to use condoms properly and with finesse.

Academy condom confidence tips

- ❶ Men should definitely try out a variety of condoms alone to discover which condom fits best.
- ❶ Different manufacturers produce varying sizes and you should look for condoms that are 'snug' enough not to leak but also not so tight that it diminishes pleasure.
- ❶ Masturbation is the perfect time to experiment as you'll be getting erect. Once you come to grips with them during self-pleasure it naturally raises your confidence to use them with a partner.
- ❶ To avoid the classic fumbling with condoms – and feeling embarrassed and inexperienced – practise as much as you need to.
- ❶ That said, there's nothing wrong with inexperience (we all begin that way!) but fumbling with a condom can kill 'the moment'.
- ❶ Women also need to do their share of homework and practise putting condoms on – a vibrator is the perfect item to practise with. Once you can slip one on your vibrator without fumbling you'll be able to help him when the time comes.

Academy homework: This weekend both male and female students will get some condoms to practise with on their own.

⦿ Condoms feel better and more natural if you pop a drop of condom-friendly lubricant inside the tip before he slips it on.

⦿ Beware of your nails and teeth piercing condoms – they must be handled with care.

⦿ Think about how you might discuss using a condom with a new lover. And definitely don't believe any excuses for not using them. Men in particular will try it on with, 'Don't you think I look "clean"?' Even the 'cleanest-looking' person in the world can have an STI.

⦿ Practise a confident reply like, 'I care about my sexual health – and yours – so you need to wear a condom.'

⦿ No one should argue with you about using condoms with STIs so rife. If they argue with you they're not worth sleeping with.

⦿ Women should bear in mind that keeping condoms with you doesn't make you a slut – it makes you smart.

⦿ Always read the instructions on condom packets for individual details. For example, some are more durable and better for anal sex. If you haven't used them for a while check their sell-by dates.

Academy motto: No glove, no love!

Lesson 3: Pole positions

Sexology research shows that over time couples slip into a favoured one or two positions. This can be relaxing knowing you can slip into position easily and comfortably. The problem? Many people confide they get bored always doing the same thing.

There are so many positions that this should never happen. It's not as if couples have to try difficult positions; often their own favourite can be modified quite easily by, for example, the man trying a slightly different angle.

Academy rule no. 16: No couple should feel pressure to swing from the proverbial chandeliers but occasionally they should make time for some pleasurable position 'road-testing'.

A study list for positions:

- If one of you is resistant to trying new positions, explore why – do they have body image issues and don't want to try anything where they're quite exposed? Many women confide that they don't like Doggy style because they don't like their bottoms being on display.

- There are always ways of using subtle lighting and loving words to help sort out such worries. If they might feel vulnerable in some other way it's worth getting to the bottom of their anxieties – sex-perimentation will be more fun if you do.

- If you can't get to grips with the issue between you then check out the following Lecture Series on communication and sexual confidence.

- Men often have real concerns that a particular position might over-stimulate them and they'll ejaculate too quickly. Obviously men don't want to disappoint their partner and shouldn't feel the pressure to use that position – or try using that PC muscle to slow down!

- Likewise both men and especially women might find certain positions under-stimulate them and it takes too long to climax. A major myth about male sexuality is that they can climax anytime, anywhere – it's simply not true.

◗ Ideally both men and women should use positions that mimic the sensations they get from masturbation. Technically speaking penetration is actually the man 'masturbating' himself inside her vagina and her 'masturbating' herself against parts of him like his pubic bone or the base of his penile shaft. You wouldn't waste time on masturbatory techniques that didn't work – equally if people find a position doesn't work then they shouldn't waste time persisting with it.

◗ There isn't any rule that states once you've started with a position you have to stay in it until you both orgasm. Moving from one position to another during sex can feel fantastic and add to your excitement.

◗ There also isn't any rule that states you can't start one position, go back to some foreplay, and restart in another position. Sometimes that's easier than moving from one position directly into another.

◗ If you both decide to try a new position and it doesn't work, then never see that as a failure. It's a success because you were both happy to try something new. We're far too judgemental about things like that – it's better to try and find that it's not satisfying than to wonder what other position might be fun.

◗ It's a fact that during different life phases a different position may work better for you. If she's pregnant you might find your old position isn't do-able. Or if one of you has an accident and perhaps breaks a leg you'll undoubtedly find you need to work around this and try new positions. Unless you want to be sex-free for the three months of wearing a cast.

Additional learning: Different cultures have different ideas about sex. For instance, the Taoists in China believe that life is fluid and so movement during sex should also be fluid – essentially couples should move from one position to another to see what brings the most pleasure.

Academy fact: Ultimately different positions suit different sizes and shapes; different levels of flexibility and stamina. This is why you might have found one position worked fantastically with an ex-partner but doesn't work with your new partner.

Academy note for the smaller man: If you're a man who worries about your size when erect it's important to choose positions where her vagina naturally tightens up. When describing a position I'll point out if it's a good one for the slightly less well-endowed man to try.

Here is a list of some classic positions as well as some more sophisticated and challenging ones. Have fun reading through them, thinking about which might be good to try. Don't get caught up worrying about moving into a new position; it's always critical to go 'with the moment' during sex so that you let go and truly enjoy it.

Switch off from distractions and simply enjoy the sensations you get from whatever position you're in. Stay open-minded about trying new positions and always be considerate to your partner's needs when experimenting.

The Missionary – Let's begin with this classic position: the woman lies on her back and the man lies on top of her between her legs. Although many joke it's old hat and lacklustre, it's still the most popular position for couples.

A couple has good eye contact with each other in this position, which can be very satisfying and develop intimacy. With small variations they can create new sensations.

Academy spicy-position tip: If flexible, the woman can wrap her legs around his waist. If they add a cushion to slip underneath her bottom she'll get even more lift and he can get deeper penetration.

If she isn't that flexible she can try wrapping one leg around his knees, thighs or waist (again depending on flexibility) – this will create further sensations because it tightens her vaginal muscles.

The CAT (The Coital Alignment Technique, or as some call it the Clitoral Alignment Technique) – This must-try has a great success rate for two main reasons: it facilitates a woman's orgasm and it's just so simple.

Although she can either be on the bottom or on top, most women report being on top definitely helps them reach climax. So, beginning with the woman on top, she faces her partner with her legs either inside or outside of his. If she has her legs inside his it squeezes his penis tightly so she should take care how much additional pressure she uses.

She now moves 'upwards' on his pubic bone a couple centimetres so that her clitoral region rubs his pubic bone. He should give her 'permission' to move in the way that best stimulates her clitoris. This might be with small circular or thrusting movements that mimic the sensations she gets during masturbation.

The CAT is ideal as the primary position or even the second or third position when both partners are fully stimulated and she's getting nearer to climax. It ensures he slows down so he doesn't reach orgasm too quickly and allows her to concentrate on achieving the right stimulation to finally reach orgasm. If they're honest, men find they like it because it allows them a bit of a rest unless she goes underneath him and he's on top.

Academy spicy-position tip: Take time and enjoy the slow sensuality of the CAT. He can tickle her fancy by reaching around her bum and between her upper thighs to stroke her perineum and labia. If she's comfortable with this extra stimulation it'll definitely help bring her to orgasm.

The Reverse Missionary – This is actually the other version of the CAT with her legs moving from in between his to outside of his. Some people call this the Reverse Missionary because it's exactly like the classic Missionary but with her on top.

It's perfect to move into if he's getting over-excited because of the pressure on his penis from the classic CAT or if her legs feel strained in between his. The Reverse Missionary takes the pressure off him and she can continue to stimulate her clitoral region.

Academy spicy-position tip: For a variation in sensations try **The Interlace** position. She keeps one leg between his two legs and moves her other leg to outside his leg. The extra sensations come from her body being slightly angled over his – this puts pressure back on his penis. He can continue gently stroking her labia and perineum with his fingers for extra pleasure. Or he can use a vibrator on her anus and perineum in this position.

The Cradle – You can easily move into this from the last positions. In this position she remains on top, lying chest against chest but she draws her legs up underneath her so her knees are bent. It's named the Cradle because it's as if she's cradling his body with her body.

This is a perfect position for slow and sensual thrusting and allows lots of touching and kissing.

Academy spicy-position tip: If she wants she can reach under his hips and cradle his buttocks to steady them – particularly if his thrusting gets vigorous. And because she ends up with a slightly raised bottom in this position it allows him to slip his hand between their pelvises and gently nudge/stroke her clitoral region.

The Cradle

The Cow Girl (also called The Lovers' Seat) – Either begin in this position or move into it from something like the CAT. She gets into a 'sitting' position on top of him and he lies flat on his back. You can have loads of fun with this position and it's perfect for a 'boob-man' as he has great access to her breasts and can play with them during sex. She should also caress his chest or touch her own breasts as they'll be in full view.

The Cow Girl

She gently glides up and down as passion builds. He steadies the action by holding her hips. This is perfect for her to control the pace of things. Unless she's quite fit her thighs can get tired as she raises herself up and down. To make it easier she can stop moving up and down and go for more of a slow grind. If she has low body confidence a dimmer switch or candles will provide subtle lighting.

Academy spicy-position tip: She can get a little creative by alternating between raising herself up and down a few times, and then reverting to the slower, circular grinds. The Cow Girl allows the couple more intensity and intimacy to look each other in the eye. Riding off into the sunset takes on a new meaning!

The Spinner – Moving from the Cow Girl she turns sideways while sitting on top of him. This may seem a little uncomfortable at first with the penis angled slightly awkwardly inside her, but as she continues to 'spin' another ninety degrees she ends up with her back facing him.

From here she can change the pressure of penetration by varying the way she sits. Leaning forward with her hands onto his ankles decreases the pressure between them. While leaning back, resting her hands at the sides of his chest will increase the pressure on his penis.

This is a flexible position and it's easy to vary sensations. As a bonus, it doesn't require a lot of strength from either partner. He might want to hold her hips to maintain penetration so he doesn't slip out, though.

Academy spicy-position tip: Slipping her feet underneath herself (with knees bent), while supporting herself with her hands, she can then raise and lower herself up and down on his penis with her back still towards him. This variation is known as 'offering the moon' with a reference to 'mooning' because her bottom moves up and down in full view of him. He'll love this if he's a so-called bum man!

The Spoons – A couple can begin in the Spoons position or move into it from the Spinner: he can hold her hips and together they can ease carefully sideways onto the bed. Done gently it can be done without him withdrawing his penis, so take your time easing into this new position.

The Spoons position is versatile and ideal for a slow, sensual and lazy sex session or for more vigorous ones. Alternatively a couple can slip into this position when they've been having vigorous sex and need to slow down. The man lies on his side, behind his lover with the curve of her back and bottom snuggled into the curve of his stomach and chest. She's also on her side and lifts her upper leg a little to allow him to penetrate.

A little movement, usually with her pushing her bottom back and upwards a bit, will help him easily enter her. Thrusting can be gentle or vigorous depending on the mood.

Academy spicy-position tip: It's easy for him to carry on with foreplay. With his arm wrapped over her – or slipped through underneath her arm – he can run his hands over her erogenous zones. He can also kiss and gently lick and nuzzle the back of her neck. Such continued foreplay is a big turn-on for her.

If their hips are angled correctly this is a good position for stimulating her G-spot. Without further clitoral stimulation many women won't reach orgasm in this position, no matter how much they enjoy it. So either she or he can stimulate her clitoris or clitoral region (whatever her preference) with fingers or a vibrator. She may not have the confidence to do this without him encouraging her to touch herself as he continues thrusting.

Sensations can vary the higher she lifts her upper leg – the higher she lifts it the more he can curve his pelvis into her vaginal region, getting deeper penetration. She can even raise her upper leg and then bend it at the knee to wrap around his upper leg to hold him tightly in place when thrusting gets faster.

Lovers' Embrace – A couple can easily move into this position from the Spoons with her simply turning around to face him. Likewise, they can move into it from the Missionary or if she's on top of him. Lie on your sides facing each other, embracing. She lifts her upper thigh to allow him to slide into her.

To vary the sensations between them she can move her leg further up or close it back down more tightly on his leg. This varies the pressure. Alternatively, for a lot of friction she can clasp her legs onto his completely. This added pressure on his penis is good for a man who's on the small size.

Academy spicy-position tip: Their hands can wander over each other's backs and bums, cupping each other's buttocks so that the pressure of his thrusting doesn't push them apart.

Lovers' Snake – She lies on her back as he lies on his side, at her side. Twisting slightly at her waist she allows her bent legs to 'rest' over his hips. He can use one arm to reach across her lower stomach and hold the far side of her hips. He then begins penetration from this slightly sideways angle. This position allows a couple to keep caressing each other.

Academy spicy-position tip: Their movements will be slow and sensuous and he'll be able to fondle her breasts for extra pleasure.

Lovers' Knot – A more complicated position that starts with him sitting either in an armchair or on the edge of a bed – but he needs to be stable or have the strength to maintain stability. She sits on his lap facing him, straddling his hips so his penis can penetrate her.

Thrusting is slow and sensual, especially if he's in an

armchair – a position for a couple who want to take their time. If he's sitting on the edge of the bed she can more easily wrap her legs tightly around his waist.

Academy spicy-position tip: Kissing and caressing can definitely continue, and as a seated position opens up her bottom quite a bit he can give her a bit of anal-play if she likes it.

The Monkey – This position is for the experienced couple or at least where one partner is confident about trying it. It is good for both vaginal and anal penetration. The couple can move into this from another position or once he's turned on from foreplay.

The Monkey

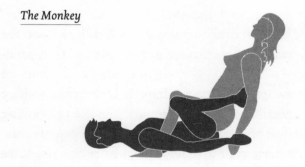

He lies on his back and bends his knees to his chest. She then gently sits back on to his erection. She rests her arms slightly behind her so that he can hold them – this requires some balance and strength on his part. His feet press into her upper back for support – almost as if they provide support for her like the back of a chair.

Academy spicy-position tip: Their movements must be slow and sure but this position is an incredible turn-on for those who enjoy something different and erotic.

Split the Whisker – He crouches on his knees as she lies on her back. She rests one leg on his shoulder – so it requires flexibility on her part. The Split the Whisker position gives him good control. He holds her thighs, hips or knees, in order to keep stability and not slip out of her.

A couple can either do this position in bed or on the floor – as long as his knees are comfortable because he'll be crouching. Most men love the view with this position – they get a good view of her vulva and find that a big turn-on. This is also exciting for sexually confident women who like to show off their bodies. If only all women felt this way!

Academy spicy-position tip: He can pull her hips slightly up his thighs which might allow access to the G-spot in some women.

The Ploughman – This position is similar to Split the Whisker, except she removes her leg from his shoulder, bending her knee so that her heel rests towards her bottom – at the side of his hip. He's still kneeling. He can raise himself up slightly higher by leaning gently against her knee and pulling her hips slightly higher up his thighs for deeper penetration.

Although movement probably has to be slow – unless he has excellent control – the benefit is he can thrust deeply.

Academy spicy-position tip: If he feels in good control resting on one arm, he can use the other hand to gently fondle her anal area and perineum.

The Starfish – A couple can move into this position from Split the Whisker or even classic Missionary if she brings both her knees towards her chest. She rests her feet either side of his chest or on top of his shoulders if she's flexible. He can vary the sensations by holding her knees and opening or closing them a bit.

The Starfish name comes from her appearing to be like a

starfish with her knees or feet sticking outwards, supported by his kneeling posture. She does need to be flexible to manage this position. And he needs to be relatively fit to maintain control of the thrusting because she's pretty much stationary. He can hold her hands or he can lean on his arms on the bed. For a man who likes to control a position this is a good one.

Academy spicy-position tip: By slowing up his thrusting, deepening it, or varying the style (straight thrusts to circular, etc.) he can give her amazing sensations. He can of course move slowly and sensually and build intimacy with good eye contact in the Starfish.

The Starfish

Unfold the Flower – This position needs a little more finesse and flexibility than the Starfish. She opens up from the Starfish by resting the backs of her legs or knees on his shoulders. He continues to kneel, his knees apart with her hips pulled inwards between them.

For a flexible and trusting couple this position allows very deep penetration.

Academy spicy-position tip: Although skimpy thongs aren't as popular as they once were, for extra spice she can wear a silky thong that he can slip aside so he can enter her vagina for penetration. Many men like the 'tugging' sensation of a thong pulling against their shaft during thrusting.

The Swing – He lies flat on his back with his knees bent at right angles. She gets astride him facing his knees and sits on to his erection with her inner thighs squeezing his thighs. She can place her hands on his knees to steady herself. They can both move together gently – or if she wants to and is physically fit, she can start moving more vigorously while he holds her bottom steady.

Academy spicy-position tip: He should definitely arouse her further by massaging her bum cheeks.

The Courtesan – She sits on a lowish chair or at the end of the bed. He kneels in front of her on the floor facing her. She lifts her legs carefully and wraps them around his lower back. He steadies her by holding her around her waist – when ready he can begin gentle thrusting.

Academy spicy-position tip: This is an excellent position to continue kissing and sensuous cuddling, and he has good access to sucking her nipples.

Seated Embrace – He sits with his legs crossed – for a sense of support he might decide to have his back against the wall or he can sit on the bed and lean against the headboard. As she eases into his lap and wraps her legs around his back, this will push his back away from the wall or headboard. This position is very sensual and loving and it's easy to continue kissing each other during gentle thrusting.

Academy spicy-position tip: While they embrace and move gently he can nuzzle behind her ears and neck – incredibly sensuous for her.

The Pillar – He needs a lot of strength and coordination for this position, but it's very satisfying if he can manage it. He kneels on the ground and she slips onto him, facing him. She holds on to his neck as he slips his penis inside her. He steadies her by wrapping his arm around her lower back. They can both control gentle thrusting. This position gets its name because if the couple moves in time together they almost form a 'pillar' shape as they're quite upright.

Academy spicy-position tip: If she likes little slaps on her bottom he can give her the occasional slap in this position.

The Crouching Tiger – An unusual but satisfying position that's best done on the floor rather than in bed. This is a great one if you're messing around on your sofa: then you can move onto the floor to do it. It takes some coordination and strength.

He crouches with his knees bent and angles himself over her. She is essentially balanced on her bottom with her legs slung over his crouching thighs. He can steady her by holding her waist or her shoulders. If she's flexible enough she can slip her feet against his chest as in the Starfish. The 'counter-pressure' a couple gets in this position helps him control his thrusting. They can also use the sofa with cushions for support with her leaning her back on it. For easier access and more comfort she can sit slightly raised on a couple of cushions.

Academy spicy-position tip: She needs all her concentration for this but if she's well balanced she can stroke the top of her pubic mound and clitoral region for extra pleasure as he moves.

The Lotus – As the name suggests he sits in the Lotus position (or semi-Lotus) if he's flexible. This is the perfect position for gaining intimacy because you're looking directly into the other's eyes. Facing each other, they draw their bottoms together as she slips her legs over his. If she's flexible she can wrap them around his lower back; otherwise she rests her feet on the floor behind him.

He has to enter slowly and move gently. Active thrusting isn't possible but deep penetration definitely is. As with the Crouching Tiger above, for easier access and more comfort she can sit slightly raised on a couple of cushions, otherwise he may feel his penis is being bent slightly downwards during penetration.

The couple rocks gently together and towards each other – with these moves they can create subtle yet hot sensations. Some women find they get extra G-spot stimulation in the Lotus.

Academy spicy-position tip: During the gentle rocking the couple can reach around and caress each other's buttocks and he might be able to reach her anal area for extra pleasure. This position is a great one for the smaller man.

Easy Rider – From the Lotus position a couple can move into the Easy Rider. He kneels and pulls her up on to his lap, so she's sitting astride him. Her feet support some of her weight and they can slip more cushions under her bottom to help support her.

In this position the man won't feel too much downwards pressure on his penis. All they need to do is a gentle rocking motion that will prevent him from coming too quickly. Again she gets deep penetration in this position. You can use a version of Easy Rider on a sofa or big easy chair. He gets seated as she gets on him for an easy ride!

Academy spicy-position tip: He can nuzzle and kiss her breasts and nipples for extra stimulation.

Good Old-Fashioned 'Doggy' – I'd love to rename this position but everyone knows it as 'Doggy' style. She is on the bed or floor on all fours as he kneels behind her. The couple can put pillows under her stomach for comfort and support.

This position is fantastic for G-spot stimulation as his deep penetration can hit the front wall of her vagina. Also while balancing with one hand he can reach around and stimulate her clitoris/clitoral region with the other. Alternatively she can self-stimulate with her fingers.

If your bed has a headboard, manoeuvre so that she leans on this with her hands for a slightly different feel. In this variation he rises up slightly and can even grasp the headboard for support if he wants to quicken his pace. This position is so versatile and great for a quickie in the sitting room, for example, where she kneels on the floor – she'll probably want pillows under her knees.

Doggy is a great position for the smaller man. He can pull on her hips firmly, tilted upwards and towards his thrusting penis so he gives her good stimulation. With her being held in place at this angle it allows him to use very short but sexy strokes.

Academy spicy-position tip: For sex-tra pleasure he can stroke or slap her buttocks as long as she likes that. He should tell her how amazing her bum looks in this position – guaranteed she'll probably want to do Doggy more often.

Kneeling Dog – A variation on this theme where she kneels on the floor resting her hands – or her arms – on the sofa or bed edge. He kneels behind her and takes her Doggy style. He can reach his arms around her to play with her breasts, stomach or clitoral region.

Academy spicy-position tip: For more stimulation for her, he should try using a vibrator as he reaches around her. He can stroke her clitoral region with the vibrator in time to his gentle thrusting.

The Rocking Chair – You need to be strong for this position. A couple can move into this from Doggy style or from any rear-entry variation. He sits back completely on his knees with his upper body upright while she slides her whole pelvis back over his thighs. She pushes her bottom and genitals right into his pelvis.

The Rocking Chair

Next she bends her legs so she can reach around with her calves and grip around his back while he reaches under and around her breasts. Obviously she needs to be flexible for this. All he has to do is rock her gently. As long as they're well balanced this position is a unique one. It's perfect for a woman who gets turned on feeling his muscular power and control since he's in complete control.

Academy spicy-position tip: In this position they can only do a slow and sensual rocking motion – positioned correctly it hits her clitoral region perfectly. As he holds under her breasts he can gently squeeze them in a pulsating way in time with his thrusting.

The Resting Dog – If either of you get tired in Doggy or Rocking Chair, change into the Resting Dog. She begins in Doggy style on hands and knees but allows her hands to slip forwards so that her hips come down nearer to the mattress, tipping her pelvis more upright. The man can slip down a bit, altering his leg placement so he carries on penetrating from behind while resting on his hands. Usually his hands can rest on top of hers.

Academy spicy-position tip: She can reach between her thighs to stroke or hold the base of his penis. Or she can caress the 'million-dollar spot' on his perineum (more on that in Lecture Series 8).

Classic '69' – You need flexibility for this position but if you've been doing oral sex '69' then move into this position. Already 'top to toe' with each other, she rolls on to her back and he eases on top of her, supporting himself with his elbows and hands. He gently angles his penis into her to start partial penetration.

Try moving into this position from classic 'missionary' with the man gently moving first 90 degrees so that he's sideways on to her and angled inside her. Then he shifts a further 90 degrees so that he's 'top to toe' with his penis still inside her. Take it slow – either he or she might find the angle of the penis uncomfortable in this position. For the man who likes his bottom/anal zone touched this gives her access.

Classic '69'

Academy spicy-position tip: Try using your favourite sex toys on each other while in the 69. This is easy to do when you're both lying on your sides. You have a great view of exactly what you're stimulating with the end of the vibrator – around and around, back and forth, up and down, with little movements.

The Strip Search – She leans against a wall, in a standing position, her back to him. He enters from behind – leaning a hand against the wall for support or wrapping his arms around her waist to hold her tight. Double her sensations by nuzzling the back of her neck as he gently moves. Plus he can 'search' her with his free hand roaming her body. She should keep her high heels on – it's sexy and it makes it easier for him to start the action.

Academy spicy-position tip: Perfect for starting some fantasy-play, he can pretend he's a rather naughty detective and she's a sexy suspect who needs 'searching' from behind.

The Puppet

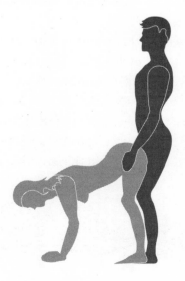

The Puppet – This is a variation of Strip Search but she moves away from the wall she's been leaning on and gently 'falls' forward from the waist as if to touch the floor (like a puppet whose strings have been dropped). She needs to be flexible for this, but it allows him fantastic G-spot access.

He holds her firmly by the hips so she feels well-supported. The Puppet is also a good position for the woman who likes to feel his penis have contact with her cervix – which requires deep penetration.

Academy spicy-position tip: Here come those gentle slaps again – he can give her extra erotic stimulation with light slaps or smacks to her buttocks.

The Wheelbarrow – From the Puppet you can move into the Wheelbarrow, but you both need to be fit. She's still bent at the waist with him behind her. Depending on how strong he is, he picks up one or both of her legs as she leans on to the floor with her hands. Or she can rest her full forearms on the ground.

The Wheelbarrow

The wheelbarrow is incredibly hot for him as it opens up her vulva for him to see 'all', so she'll need to be body-confident. Because it takes strength a couple can experiment with it for just a few thrusts before moving into another position.

Academy spicy-position tip: Even for a few thrusts it can be worth it for him if he wants to have a rather exciting view of her!

Stand and Deliver – Here's another variation on a standing position. This time she stands with her back resting against the wall. With the couple facing each other, he starts penetration as she is supported by leaning on the wall. He'll need to bend his knees and angle his hips forward in order to slip into her.

Academy spicy-position tip: It's sexy and perfect for this position for her to keep her high heels on while he's barefoot. This means his pelvis is a little lower then hers, making penetration easier.

The Lift – In this standing position she rests her foot on the bed or a chair while they hold on to each other. This will lift her pelvis slightly and opens her legs, allowing easier penetration for him. There's something quite erotic about this position and it works best, as with most standing positions, for her to keep her high heels on. Again he needs to use good control and should probably hold on to her hips while thrusting so that he doesn't slip out.

Academy spicy-position tip: She can clasp her hands on his bottom and caress his cheeks during thrusting.

The Sling – This position is interchangeable with the Lift as you can easily move from one to the other. Again standing and facing each other, he slings an arm underneath the leg that she's lifted up (in The Lift she's rested her foot on a chair or bed). This gives him some control while thrusting. Depending on how flexible she is he can raise or lower the arm that is slung under her knee to give her maximum comfort.

If she's flexible he can raise her leg high, giving him great access during penetration.

Academy spicy-position tip: She needs to hold on to him with one hand but can use her free hand to stroke her inner thighs and clitoral region and around the base of his penis.

Lovers' Clasp – This is only for skilled and super fit couples! He stands with his back to a wall as she wraps her legs around his and places her feet against the wall to support her. As he pulls back on her hips, holding her bottom, he rocks back and forth into her.

Lovers' Clasp

They both need strength for this position but it can be varied with her placing one foot down on the ground – if she's flexible. Alternatively she can try standing on both feet, rising up on her toes or in high heels. For support he leans back into the wall lowering his hips in order to achieve penetration.

Academy spicy-position tip: Since movements and thrusting need to be slow and sure, they can enjoy a long, slow passionate kiss during this position.

Staging Post – For an active couple who like to move between positions, this is a good one to try if you've been leaning on the wall but want to end up in bed. It's halfway between Strip Search and Doggy positions. Let's say she's been leaning on the wall, she can then move over to the bed and lean on the bedstead or headboard. Alternatively she can kneel on the edge of the mattress. He stays behind her and moves his hips so penetration continues. With this change of position he can thrust more vigorously.

Academy spicy-position tip: As he has quite a bit of control he can also try some 'circular' thrusts to give her some fantastic G-spot pleasuring.

The Straddle

The Straddle – A couple could move into this from the Staging Post position; he sits on the edge of the bed and she straddles him sitting back onto his erection with her back to him. He can use slow and sensual thrusting and she can use the floor to support her feet so she controls the pace and depth of thrusting.

Academy spicy-position tip: As she sits with her back to him he can reach around and use one of his hands to caress her breasts or clitoral area, using his other hand as support.

The Rider – The Rider is for very strong and flexible men only. He lies on his back on something like a big padded footstool or ottoman. With this as a support if he needs it, he arches back to the floor supporting himself with his hands – his feet planted on the other side of the footstool.

She balances one foot on the ground by one of his feet, and slips her other foot over his pelvis to straddle him. In his arching position his erection sticks up prominently so she can straddle it. Before she 'rides' his penis she can tease and stroke his testicles.

She begins gently moving on it. This is a great position for couples who strive to try new sensations. Even if physically fit, a couple might only want stay in it for a couple of minutes before changing to another position.

There is a variation for women who are very flexible and strong, where the man becomes the 'rider'. She arches over something for support like a large padded footstool. He then crouches/kneels between her legs and begins penetration while holding on to her hips to support her.

Academy spicy-position tip: While she's arched backwards and completely exposed to him, he can give her some oral sex before he begins penetration.

Easy Over – A great position for some spontaneous passion if she's flexible and they're both moderately strong. Let's say you've been getting sexy on the sofa and have undressed each other. Move to the back of an armchair (preferably, as this will give more support) or the sofa. He helps her up to sit on the back of the armchair. He takes her hands and eases her over slowly so that her head and shoulders come to rest on the seat of the chair/sofa. In this position her hips/pelvis are still on the back of the chair while her shoulders and head are snuggled into the seat.

He holds her in place as he gently starts thrusting. This position can be maintained for as long as her head and shoulders are well supported with cushions in the seat of the chair.

Academy spicy-position tip: He can pause between thrusts and caress her clitoral region, since it's completely exposed in this position.

The Mount – In this variation of the Easy Over she sits (mounts) the back of the armchair or sofa but doesn't slide her head and shoulders into the seat. As she sits there he can support her with his arms and begin thrusting. He can steady her by holding her hips or the back of the chair.

Academy spicy-position tip: Because he's doing the 'work' and supporting her, she can reach around and hold or caress his bum cheeks for added stimulation.

A final word on positions – don't forget that you can enjoy a bit of sex-play while moving between positions or taking time out from a position. While moving from one position to another your hands can roam over your partner's body, you can begin kissing again and definitely whisper to your partner how fantastic it all feels.

Academy homework: **Try a new position from this list in your next sex session.**

Lesson 4: The great climax guide – how to bring her to oh-oh-heaven!

Despite some women being better at communicating about sex than men, many women don't reach climax with their partners. It's no reflection on either of them and largely down to two things:

1/ The clitoral region must receive adequate stimulation for her to reach orgasm as it's the very rare woman who can have an orgasm without this. Because women are all constructed slightly differently, it's a matter of luck if they fit perfectly with their partner and his pubic bone stimulates her clitoris during penetration.

2/ The next issue is largely about her willingness to say what feels good and what works for her. There'll be many lessons in Lecture Series 5 on communication and confidence that'll help women who haven't been communicating their 'orgasm needs'.

Academy fact: **At any given time somewhere in the region of 70 per cent of women having sex aren't reaching climax. And only about 15 per cent climax regularly. Those statistics equal a whole load of disappointment. But here at Sex Academy we plan to change this, starting today.**

Here are some beginner pointers that every good student should learn to help the woman reach orgasm. The first section is for the girls (but the guys should study it too!):

◐ Reject thoughts that you'll 'never climax' – it's easy to slip into a negative mindset when you've never climaxed with a man.

◐ Even if you're with a partner where it's never happened, tell yourself: 'I'm going to start afresh and be positive – it can happen if I relax about it!'

◐ Women should know how their body works. The best way forward is letting your fingers do the walking through self-pleasure (masturbating). Men are masters of this – it's high time women became the mistresses of their bodies too.

◐ Self-pleasure, as noted in Lecture Series 1, arms you with knowledge you can then share with a partner.

Understanding your body + sharing that knowledge = climax guaranteed!

◐ Share the sensations you discover with him the next time you're together.

And for the guys:

◐ Sorry guys, you may think you're Mr Lover Man, but what you think works may not work for her.

◐ Help her relax and tell her to take her time.

◐ Ask her what you can do to help bring her along.

◐ She might feel embarrassed because it takes time to climax but reassurance will go a long way.

◐ Really listen to her suggestions – hopefully she knows what works for her, she just needs to share it.

◐ Don't get stressed out if it takes some time getting to know what works for her. Treat it as sex-perimentation!

Academy rule no. 17: **Female students shouldn't fake orgasms – it seems OK when you don't want to 'hurt his feelings' because you're tired and it's just not going to happen. But in the long run honesty's best. There's nothing wrong with enjoying sex-play knowing you're too tired for it to end in a climax.**

And this holds true for the men who sometimes fake orgasm – yes, believe it or not men sometimes fake it. They can do so if they're using condoms – if they haven't ejaculated because they're too tired, perhaps. They can easily pretend they have and then dispose of the condom. She'll never see that he hasn't ejaculated.

Throughout *Sex Academy* there are many tips to bring her to orgasm – here are a few to get started with:

- ❍ Use lashings of foreplay on her.
- ❍ Take your time showering her with kisses. Definitely kiss around the back of her neck and ears – unless she's super sensitive this is oh-oh-heavenly.
- ❍ Stroke her lightly with your fingers – you build more sexual tension swirling them gently all over her body. Build to a firmer touch, checking that she wants it.
- ❍ Pretend you're her 'sex doctor' discovering what makes her 'feel better'. Turning exploring her body into foreplay will get her halfway there.
- ❍ Keep asking her what feels good and where.
- ❍ When you're both ready for full sex let her select the position from those outlined above.
- ❍ Give her 'permission' to take charge of the action. Remember you can always have your pleasure once she has hers!

Academy rule no. 18: **A wise student doesn't buy into the myth that a couple must orgasm together. It's not true – there's no sex**

rule-book that says that climaxing together makes it better, so don't put yourself under the pressure!

Lesson 5: Location, location, location

Academy motto: **Variety is the spice of life**

Forget estate agents when you think of location, location, location (unless you work an estate agent scenario into fantasy-play) because location is one of the simplest ways to keep sex exciting between you.

We're very influenced by our surroundings, so it's one of the easiest ways to stop things getting boring. If a couple had sex once a week choosing a different position and sometimes throwing in a new location they could do something different every week for three or four years easily.

Far too many couples always have sex in bed. When you always have sex in the same place you're most likely to slip into the same position time after time. Even the fact that your surroundings are identical every time you have sex – the sheets, pillow coverings, the lighting, all remain the same – means that things can feel dull.

Students should put a little effort into thinking about location so they don't have the same sex in the same place over and over again. Obviously if you're in a long-term sexual relationship some routine sex is comforting and reassuring. Many partners feel emotionally connected and assured knowing they can count on some loving sex on a Sunday morning, for example.

Getting creative with locations

There are lots of places to potentially have sex as long as you're not breaking any laws – or are very careful not to get caught.

Use this list as a starting point. If you're on holiday don't ever break indecency laws in a country like Dubai, where they take physical contact in public very seriously especially if it is at all of a sexual nature. Try these:

Academy locations – level 1:

❍ Like alfresco dining, alfresco sex is out of doors under the stars. Mind you're careful no one can see what you're doing – unless of course you're dogging, in which case it's a different story.

❍ In the bath or shower with lovely warm cascades of water rushing over your bodies.

❍ On the floor – any floor – but either one that's carpeted or put down a soft blanket if it's not.

❍ Get carried away in the kitchen – but you'll definitely need something to cushion kitchen floor tiles/countertops.

❍ Say you've been working hard at your desk and want a break – maybe because you're in a hot new relationship – and lean against your desk or workstation for a quickie. Or lean against the kitchen or dining table, or the bathroom counter. Be spontaneous when the moment takes you.

❍ Just in from an evening out? Why not have a quickie against the doorframe in your front hall.

❍ You've got in, made it past your doorframe, but can have a quickie on the landing, up the stairs, against the banister. Mind you don't have any accidents – what you lean on needs to be strong enough to support you both.

❍ Get to know the local views and park somewhere with a romantic view where you can cuddle up plus more.

❍ On a country walk find a big tree to lean against for support using any of the standing positions described above.

◑ Slip into the changing room at the beach, sports complex, local gym, etc., but make sure the coast is clear!

Academy locations – level 2:

◑ Everyone's gone home so you have the offices to yourself. Make sure you don't get caught out by the late-night cleaner.

◑ Check the other guests are in bed late at night in your holiday hotel, then slip into the Jacuzzi for a wet and wild time – don't forget the condoms!

◑ Get sex-perimental in a swimming pool – the buoyancy of the water makes things fun. Why not let the water lap around you as you go for it on a lilo in the pool. Again make sure the condom stays on.

◑ You're at a boring party and decide to nip into the bathroom for a quickie without your hosts knowing.

◑ At night you slip into the local park and try a different type of swinging.

◑ If you've been out for the day shopping, why not try some subtle fun in your car in a parking garage.

◑ If you can find one, slip into in a phone-box at night for some very cosy sex.

◑ Let the rhythm of ocean waves inspire you to try sex in the dunes. You might want a blanket under you as sand gets very annoying sticking to places the sun doesn't shine.

◑ Gazing at the stars from a deckchair at your holiday hotel? Try a bit of gentle sex as you do.

Academy locations – level 3:

◑ Time to go for some knuckle-biting adventure and get sneaky in your office during working hours. A good place to try is in the stationery cupboard, staff bathroom

or behind your locked office door if you have the nerves
for it.

- As long as you don't get caught, try some foreplay on a plane trip. If the toilet's too small slip a blanket over yourselves and enjoy some sex-play.
- If you're in the mood for a quickie press the 'close doors' button while in a lift.
- You've just shared dinner in a candlelit restaurant so why not slip into a side street for some after-dinner sex.
- Let's see if you can be so quiet while having sex in your garden shed that your neighbours sitting next door in their garden haven't a clue.
- Go for some sporting moments and do a 'Boris Becker': slip into the broom cupboard of a restaurant.
- Become a true 'easy rider' and have it away on the back of a motorcycle parked safely and securely.

Academy homework: You've already been instructed to try a new position – so now you have to come up with a new location.

A final note on location: never let the fear of failure put you off being creative. It's better to take that blanket out on the country walk and try having sex leaning against a secluded tree than not try. If it doesn't work, one of you gets anxious, and you can't get comfortable, just relax about it. In fact, have a giggle about where it went wrong.

Lesson 6: Toying with toys

Sex toys are fantastic for spicing things up. They come in all sizes, shapes and various types of 'action'. I can only begin to list some of the main types – this certainly isn't a definitive list but will give you an idea of what's available. At the end of the last Lecture Series a number of websites specialising in sex toys are provided.

Academy top tips for sex toys:

◐ Always pay attention to strict hygiene for any sex toy. For instance, if you've used a vibrator in the anal passage it should never be used on her vagina.

◐ As a couple you can keep separate sex toys for anal and vaginal use.

◐ Always pay attention to the manufacturer's recommendations for cleaning sex toys.

◐ Mind your manners when shopping for sex toys – be sensitive to how your partner might feel about particular ones. For instance, a woman should never take the largest vibrator off the shelf while telling her partner she can't wait to try such a 'big one'!

◐ Have fun shopping together and look at the huge range on offer.

◐ Many sex toys give equal pleasure to men and women so be creative and sex-periment.

◐ If you are using condoms and only have one sex toy – and want to share it – wash properly between uses. Or cover it with a condom during use that can be changed before the vibrator's used on the other partner.

◐ Why not invest in two different bags for your toys and for theirs.

◐ Definitely look carefully at the action of a vibrator before you buy it as some are disappointingly complicated. You won't get your money back!

◑ Don't use everyday items as home-made sex toys! A&E doctors have told me some terrible tales of home-made sex toys gone wrong.

◑ Double the usage with your sex toys – as well as pleasuring each other, use them for self-pleasure.

◑ Using lubricants makes vibrator-play loads of fun but definitely choose water-based lubes that won't breakdown the surface of plastic-based toys. Some lubricants are made for these purposes, like Ann Summers' Slide and Ride.

◑ As a rule of thumb vibrators shouldn't be used on one spot any longer than twenty minutes maximum. You can over-stimulate the sensitive skin of the clitoris, the anus and the genitals generally.

Sex toy studies for Academy students

Let's begin with sex toys that don't require batteries – they only require lots of fun sex-perimentation. Following these, a large selection of battery-charged toys will be described.

Anal/butt plugs – Long associated with gay pleasure because they stimulate the prostate gland, some straight men and women enjoy these too. Imagine the shape of a mini-lava lamp that holds itself in place in the rectum because of the slightly bulbous end. There are also plugs with textured surfaces that give added stimulation for those who like it.

You need to use lots of lubrication when inserting these since the anal passage doesn't lubricate itself. They come in a variety of sizes and are fun to pop in during sex for extra sensations.

You can put them in during foreplay and keep them in during full sex. You can even walk around during the day with them in if you like the stimulation and to create a bit of naughtiness between you knowing you each have one in.

Persian love beads – Long ago these were worn by women to get pleasure because they didn't have a lover. These beads come on a string which is inserted into the vagina or the anus. They move around as the user moves, giving loads of pleasurable sensations. Anal beads, as with butt plugs, can be bought in various sizes and are strung together four or five at a time. Try the new soft and pliable beads that might suit those who are extra sensitive.

Think of such sensations as being like self-administered foreplay. If you're in a relationship the gentle sensations will get you ready for full sex later on, so people often put them in before sex-play to heighten their pleasure as they move around – the beads moving around inside them too.

But here's a fantastic way to make your orgasms more powerful. Insert the anal beads as per the instructions. They'll have a safety string with which to remove them. Leave one bead outside the anus and get into one of the 'women on top' positions which make it easier for him to reach around her hips. He can pull the beads out one at a time during her orgasm, giving her an explosive experience.

Keep telling your partner what feels best – like pulling on the string slowly or quickly if that's what you prefer. The next time you use the anal beads you can return the favour when they orgasm. Or have a set for each of you so that when she's recovered from her orgasm, she can pull out his beads slowly and sensually when he reaches his climax.

Inserted anally for men they stimulate the prostate gland – having this stimulated is an experience every man should have. As with simultaneous orgasms, don't put yourselves under pressure to simultaneously remove the anal beads – one or both of you may lose concentration around the point of your climax.

Oriental love balls or eggs – Love balls or eggs are made for vaginal use and, unlike the love beads (above) which are often four on a string, they come as a pair. They're a bit larger but essentially give the same sorts of sensations. Some women might prefer one over the other.

For some extra pleasure ask your partner to insert them slowly and sensually for you – quite easily done since they're less fiddly then the beads. Turn it into a game where it's a secret pleasure that only the two of you know about. They'll excite and arouse you as you go about your errands for the day.

Dildos – These are simply non-vibrating penis-shaped sex toys. Some couples prefer to use these as they don't like the buzzing noise of vibrators. They're manipulated by your hand or your partner's. Dildos can stimulate the vagina or anus by being moved in and out and around and around in circular motions. They range from dildos made of lifelike plastic to those made of vibrant colours. Spoil yourself or your partner with a dildo that's encrusted with semi-precious materials from upmarket adult shops.

The Laid D1 dildo – A beautifully designed dildo from Scandinavia, this one claims to be shaped in a way that gives powerful, longer-lasting orgasms.

The accommodator – You could call this a dildo with a difference as it's rather strange-looking but has amazing powers to please her. This toy is specially designed for a man (or woman in a lesbian relationship) to wear while giving oral sex to her. Imagine a dildo shape strapped to the chin that penetrates her vagina while he licks her clitoris for double pleasure. Not for everyone!

Strap-on dildo – It's not only lesbian couples that buy strap-on dildo harnesses; nowadays over a third are purchased by straight couples. Strap-ons are fantastic for fantasy-play – many who feel inhibited about being penetrated with a strap-on will let go of their inhibitions if it's part of a fantasy. This means men will play out various fantasies – particularly of giving up control – while being penetrated by her.

If the idea of screwing him with a strap-on turns you on, but you don't want him to feel threatened, bring it up tactfully. Strap-ons require practice, so don't give up as many couples do on their first attempt. Begin very slowly and carefully, using gentle thrusts until you get used to doing it. Then you can adjust them as you go until you've got into a rhythm.

Some strap-ons designed for lesbians include a dildo for the wearer. As one woman penetrates her partner she's also penetrated. Definitely make sure your strap-on fits well or you risk losing the pleasure of the experience.

Double-ended dildos – Again these are versatile and can be used in lesbian love or by straight couples: double-ended dildos can penetrate her vagina and anus at the same time, or penetrate two women's vaginas at the same time, or penetrate her vagina or anus and his anus at the same time.

It may be hard to imagine, but the two people using a double-ended dildo shunt their genitals towards each other so that they can be penetrated at the same time. One way of making this easier is to sit facing each other and move your genitals so they meet – for instance having her legs over his. If the man's to be anally penetrated he can lie back and twist on his side for one end to be inserted. She can stay seated or lie back too.

Once you have the double-ended dildo inside both of you, begin moving gently together with a slight rocking action.

This way you both share the pleasure of the two 'heads' inside you at the same time.

Saturn crystal wand – These are gorgeous to look at with some lovely lumps and bumps for sensual stimulation. They'll reach your G-spot and A-zone and a couple can have lots of fun with them.

The Frenchy super cock – This is a large dildo with a big 'knob' that can provide good stimulation. Some might find its glow-in-the-dark style off-putting, but it has handy 'testicles' you can hold on to.

Penile shaft sleeves – These are an amazingly fun little item that some couples love; others feel the hassle is not worth the extra stimulation. The sleeves are highly flexible and soft and can be worn on the finger to manually stimulate her. Or they can be worn on the shaft of his penis for extra stimulation of the clitoris, labia and vagina during penetration.

There's a wide range of styles with a variety of ridges and textures to experiment with. Definitely use with lubricant if you're pleasuring her manually. She might love the different sensations she gets when he slides it on the base of his penis.

She can also try using a sleeve over a couple of her fingers when manually stimulating him. Definitely use them to change the sensation of any basic vibrator by slipping a sleeve on it.

Cock rings – Some men swear by cock rings, which keep the blood in the erect penis from flowing back out of it. Men who favour them report they like the sensation of the building sexual tension while wearing one.

Always follow the instructions. Most are slipped around

the base of the penis and under the testicles while holding the testicles slightly away from the body. Many men find they have a longer-lasting erection with extra firmness. There are all sorts of rings available, but I recommend using the flexible cock rings instead of the metal ones as these can 'give' for easier placement.

Have your partner help slip it on as a bit of foreplay. Don't forget to lightly lubricate it and slide it on the shaft and under the scrotum. The man should make any final adjustments as he'll know what feels most comfortable.

Couples vary in their preferences. Some enjoy the cock ring during manual sex-play. Others like it on during intercourse, sometimes removing it before he climaxes. It can also be slipped in place after penetration has started as a means of slowing things down.

Some cock rings have various attachments like clitoral or G-spot ticklers, or mini weights to give him a pulling sensation on his scrotum. Never use a cock ring for more than twenty minutes and don't worry if the penis looks darker during this period from the collected blood.

Micro rabbit stretch cock ring – This waterproof stretchy silicone ring is a great sex toy for couples. It has a multi-speed clit-tickling rabbit.

Labial spreader – This is something super different and great for the exhibitionist woman or for the man who's voyeuristic. 'Opening' her up, it can make oral sex amazing and is a great little item to spice up fantasy-play. For instance, she could be the fair maiden who is sexually 'tormented' by an evil knight.

It's held in place with straps that fasten around her upper thighs and little padded 'grips' that hold her outer labia open. How wide she opens her thighs affects how wide she is spread. Many women report increased sensations with their labia spread open. And if he goes down on her he gets loads of visual stimulation.

There are two extra benefits to a spreader: as it holds her open, her hands don't get in the way of him giving her oral pleasure and neither do his, so he can use them to give her extra stimulation.

Chastity belts – If you're into playing fantasy games then you'll love adding a chastity belt to your role-play costume collection. Some belts are beautifully made by specialist fetish shops; other, simpler ones can be bought at adult shops.

Toys that 'purr' and will make you 'purr'
Thank goodness the vibrator market is no longer dominated by the bad-taste, garishly coloured sex toys of the last generation. A lot of planning and thought go into contemporary designs that are made in more naturalistic colours as well as a huge variety of shapes – something to suit everyone's tastes.

Vibrators are fantastic for self-pleasure and also for couples to have fun with, as mentioned in previous lessons. Any woman who has difficulty reaching orgasm should definitely try using a vibrator. They can hit the spot and give you ideas of what sort of pressure and friction you need to reach climax. Many sex therapists advise experimenting with vibrators to give people the confidence to discover more about their sexual response. You have the Professor of Pleasure's permission to get some va-va-vrrrroooom into your life!

For your 'vibrator studies' why not consider trying one or two of the following:

Vibrating cock rings – In addition to the classic cock rings above, there are all sorts of vibrating ones to give him a sensational time.

Vibrating cock sleeves – As mentioned above, penile shaft sleeves give extra stimulation, but when they vibrate they give even more pleasure.

Finger-tip vibrators – These are small but perfectly formed and come in a variety of styles that are slipped on his or her finger and used to vibrate around the clitoral region. But don't stop there – they can give pleasure to the nipples, the perineum and elsewhere too!

The Zing finger – You're guaranteed to put a zing in your sex when you use this finger-sized vibrator.

The Fukuoku finger massager – A great example of the above with three different sleeves that will give you different sensations.

The Fukuoku glove – This rather pricey gadget slips on your hand to give you five fun-filled vibrating fingers.

Clitoral ticklers – These are sometimes attached to regular vibrators or can be used on their own. These vibrate but also have little attachments for added pleasure. Some are textured with little 'knobbles' or have feather-like ticklers for her clitoris.

G Art bullet – This lovely looking vibrating bullet has a clitoris-shaped cut-out. Typical of many of the bullets available, it has different vibrating and pulsing options.

The Bliss bullet – This smooth and sleek-looking vibrator is ready to travel wherever you're going because of its discreet size.

G-spot aqua vibe – This G-spot stimulator is waterproof for bathtime bliss. It's got the 'come over here' crooked-finger design to reach her G-spot and great multi-speed settings so you can go from very subtle to more powerful vibrations.

VibraExciter – This is a fun mobile accessory that's connected to a bullet vibrator. For a bit of sneaky fun you can set it so that it starts vibrating when your mobile rings. A unique feature is that the vibrations last as long as your phone call does. It also vibrates for twenty to thirty seconds when you receive a text.

Bendable vertebrae vibe – It gets its name from the big 'knobbles' running down it and its bendable quality gives perfect G-spot stimulation. Simply ignore the rather lurid colours and you'll have fun with it.

Vibrating rock chick – A great vibrator that's been around a while, its ingenious shape stimulates the G-spot as well as your clitoral region. Because its vibrations are subtle it might not be suitable for a woman who likes stronger vibes.

The Jessica Rabbit or pearl rabbit – This is a true classic and despite it being rather strange-looking, once you try it you'll probably love it. It is multi-action with the main vibrator penetrating the vagina and the little ears of the rabbit vibrating either side of her clitoris.

Multiple vibrators – Those R&D (research and design) boffins have designed some pretty incredible vibrators over the years that have anal, vaginal and clitoral stimulating heads all on one toy. These claim to give a complete sensation experience, but some women may find stimulation of all three zones at once overwhelming.

Three-way rabbit – As with the 'sister' rabbit vibrators above, this is a popular version of the multiple vibrator that tickles all three areas – your clitoris, your vagina and your anal area. Although it looks pretty ridiculous, like a lot of the rabbit toys it certainly hits the spot for many women.

G-spot vibrators – These are very popular choices because of their convenient bend which stimulates the front wall of the vagina and the elusive G-spot. Some are styled as a wand with a vibrator at the end, while others are thicker. Some women swear by these and love to be stimulated with them by their partners. For an X-rated idea you can kneel on your hands and knees, or maybe lean your hands against the sofa or end of the bed, or kneel on the bed. Have him kneel behind you and vibrate you from behind – he gets an incredibly hot view!

The Promise Vibrator – This is curved just right for G-spot stimulation and does as it promises, giving her a great time.

Liberte – This has wonderful sleek and natural contours designed to hit her G-spot. A word of warning, though: it has some powerful vibrations!

Anal vibrators – There are a huge range of anal vibrators and Ann Summers does a particularly good pleasure pack containing a number of attachments. These are great for him or for her.

Academy warning: **When using a vibrator for anal pleasure – even if it's specifically designed as an anal vibrator – make sure you don't let go of it and lose it up the anus. I've spoken to many hospital doctors who warn that these can travel far into the colon and continue to vibrate – not in a pleasurable way at this point! And this means a trip to the hospital to have it removed.**

Clitoral/pubis vibrators – These are unique egg-shaped or flat-shaped vibrators designed to 'sit' on the pubis/clitoral region and pulsate. They are great for women with difficulties reaching climax. They feel incredibly arousing and she'll be ready for full sex after being vibrated with one.

Vido V8 – A silicone toy made with Vido technology. It provides a unique sensation by distributing vibrations equally from the base to the tip of the vibrator while also pulsating. It responds as a woman clenches it and will make your PC muscle exercises go with a bang. Chargeable with a mobile-phone-style charger, it has a cylindrical carry case that's sleek and attractive.

B-doyng – A lot of cheeky fun, this vibrator can be personalised with your own filthy saying or message branded on it. Made with Vido technology (as above), its vibrating pulsations increase the tighter you hold it. For many women this creates near perfect sensations because the nearer they come to orgasm the more intense the stimulation they need.

Tongue vibrators – These vibrators are designed to make oral sex even better. They slip on his tongue and vibrate while he's giving oral sex. The Tongue Joy is a popular model. She'll love the vibrations as well as feeling his lovely wet tongue!

Pelvic toner – Not exactly a sex toy but definitely worth a try to keep your vaginal muscle in tone. Remember from earlier lessons that the stronger this muscle is, the more powerful your orgasms.

Hi-tech vibrators – These are incredibly lifelike vibrators with technology that makes them feel very much like real skin. Definitely not cheap, but look out for vibrators made with Technoskin and UR3 materials for a really lifelike experience.

Glow in the dark – Many people are shy about using sex toys and for anyone with inhibitions you can turn out the lights and use a glow-in-the-dark vibrator. As things get hot and playful you won't lose it!

Body massagers – With an enormous amount of back and neck ache around, there are many different wand-type body massagers that can be used for more than just aches and pains. These give wide, sweeping strokes that also feel amazing across the pubic zone, down the sensitive areas of the inner thighs, across the genitals and the bum cheeks.

Harness-style vibrators – A good example of these is the Butterfly, which is a fantastic device; once she tries it and gets it positioned correctly she'll probably love it. The Butterfly is strapped on to her thighs and has a central, flat vibrating area positioned over her genitals. This can give amazing sensations, especially if he strokes and caresses other erogenous zones of hers while this is vibrating.

Harnesses for him – Again, the men aren't forgotten when it comes to vibrators. Harnesses can be held in place with flexible straps – in this case slipped over his penis and testicles. These have attachments for vibrating against her during penetration. Some of these are ingeniously designed with little loops to slip in a vibrating bullet for her. Others have clit stimulators of various types.

Suspended harnesses – If you've got money to invest in one there are some great ceiling-mounted harnesses. They aim for comfort but some couples do find them uncomfortable. They usually have multiple adjustable straps, and the harness suspends her over him. They can either have full sex or he can give her some super hot oral sex. As the harnesses swivel he can easily turn her for a fresh access point.

Academy word of caution: You must follow the instructions for suspending them so your ceiling doesn't crash down on you!

The Thai basket – Another version of a suspended harness, this is suspended above the bed or floor. She sits in the basket which has an opening in the centre of the seat. This way he's got complete access to her vagina and anus.

Private pole dancing – Many couples have taken to erecting their own temporary or permanent poles. Practice makes perfect and the more practice you get the more confident you feel in flaunting your body. He can also give her a bit of a show. It's a hot way to indulge fantasies in which you work in a pole-dancing club and he's a customer who can't resist you – even though it's against the club rules.

Whips, crops, masks and other such sexy things – Some of the gear for bondage and domination will be described in

Lecture Series 8. Relevant websites will be listed at the end of book.

Slightest touch system – The electric pads in this system are attached to a woman's ankles and a current is sent up the nerves to the pelvic region. Some women claim the stimulation brings them to a pre-orgasmic state. A word of warning: this is debated by the medical profession and some think it might be a placebo effect at work or that the stimulation provides a soothing effect for these women if they've been experiencing stress.

Academy sex toy tip: Don't forget to double both of your pleasure by slipping a vibrator between you during full sex. Experiment with finding the place where at least one of you benefits from the extra stimulation.

Academy fact: Research shows that women are more likely to have a second orgasm or multiple orgasms when receiving different stimulation the second or third time around. This is yet another good reason to experiment with vibrators. Once she's had her first orgasm through manual, oral or penetrative sex, as long as she's not too sensitive, try using a vibrator to give her new sensations for a second climax.

Academy myth-buster: Women should never buy into the myth that if they don't have multiple orgasms they're a sexual failure. It's simply not true and it's better to enjoy one good orgasm than worry about many other potentially smaller ones.

A few more Academy tips on toys

If, as with many couples, he climaxes more quickly than she

does, one of the best investments you can make is a vibrator for her. When you're both in the mood he can pleasure her until she climaxes or nears that point, when they can then start full sex. This way he shouldn't get over-stimulated and climax too quickly.

If, after being stimulated with a vibrator, you start penetration and he's getting too excited, he can withdraw and pause for a few moments to get control back. In that time he can continue stimulating her with a vibrator.

Many men feel quite inhibited about saying they'd like to try the sensations of a vibrator. But why wouldn't he like to feel a vibrator running up and down his perineum and anal area? It's important couples 'normalise' such desires, and if she has a sneaky suspicion he'd like some buzzing on his bits she should suggest it.

This Lecture Series has given you plenty of ideas for physics – or getting physical with each other – to indulge in soon.

Lecture Series 4 Sex-amination

Circle the answer that you think is correct. Count up your number of A, B and C answers and then check the answer key below.

1/ _Where is the man located in classic Doggy-style position?_
   A/ _Behind the woman_
   B/ _Sideways to the woman_
   C/ _On top of the woman_

2/ _What would be a good idea to take along for having sex on the beach?_
   A/ _A blanket_
   B/ _A sun hat_
   C/ _Flippers_

3/ Where is the woman located in classic Spoons position?
   A/ In front of the man
   B/ On top of the man
   C/ Underneath the man

4/ To help a woman reach climax what would be best to do?
   A/ Give her lots of foreplay and take your time
   B/ Give her lots of foreplay
   C/ Do the same things you did to your ex who always reached
      climax

5/ Which of the following can vibrators do best?
   A/ Give added pleasure to both women and men
   B/ Give added pleasure to women
   C/ Make you laugh with their buzzing

6/ How long should a man leave a cock ring in place?
   A/ No longer than twenty minutes
   B/ No longer than sixty minutes
   C/ As long as it feels good

7/ A vibrator should never be used for longer than...
   A/ Twenty minutes in any given spot
   B/ Sixty minutes in any given spot
   C/ There is no time limit to this pleasure

8/ What position is highly recommended for a woman who doesn't
   climax easily?
   A/ The CAT – the coital alignment technique
   B/ Missionary position
   C/ Any standing position

9/ *Can lubricants be used with vibrators?*
   A/ *Yes, as long as they are water-based*
   B/ *Yes, definitely*
   C/ *No, why would you use lubricant with a vibrator?*

10/ *Which position is great for giving her G-spot stimulation?*
   A/ *Doggy-style position*
   B/ *Spoons position*
   C/ *Missionary position*

Number of As: _____

Number of Bs: _____

Number of Cs: _____

◖ Mainly As: Astoundingly hot

You are a hot one and have clearly paid attention! Your technique is climbing to higher and higher heights and you shouldn't have any problems satisfying a partner.

◖ Mainly Bs: Could pay more attention in lectures

Granted, this is a fairly detailed Lecture Series and you've struggled a bit. If you're feeling confident by all means move on to the next Lecture Series, but if not, feel free to scan through again and pick up more detail from these lessons.

◖ Mainly Cs: Needs to try much harder

Where has your concentration been? If your poor score is due to simply not memorising the names of positions, say, then that's OK. What counts is that you actually know how to get in and out of them – as long as you can do that, you can call them whatever you want to.

The Big 'C' Words – Confidence & Communication Skills: How to Get What You Want

Now students will cover the all-important 'C' words. No sniggering among Academy students – I'm talking about everything to do with increasing your sexual *confidence* to get what you want, to overcome bedroom inhibitions and to feel confident pleasuring a partner. Plus we'll cover sexual *communication* and how to talk about anything.

There's such interplay between sexual confidence and communication that you might cover them as one set of lessons. Obviously higher confidence means you're happier to communicate your sexual preferences. And if you have good communication skills you feel more confident anyway. However, I've always found if you build sexual confidence first it's far easier to put into action communication techniques. So we'll cover these lessons in that order.

Step by step I'll provide practical advice to slowly build your confidence and boost your communication skills. You'll find a lot of the principles also apply to your life outside of the bedroom.

Lesson 1: Building sexual confidence

Sexual confidence, like general confidence, varies tremendously between people. Some take knock-backs in life – and in the bedroom – as if they hadn't happened. Things wash over them like water off the proverbial duck's back. Others find it hard to cope with any setback in life and their low self-confidence is magnified in the bedroom, where they feel especially inhibited, embarrassed and lacking in confidence.

Most fall between these two extremes, but even people with moderate confidence might lack sexual confidence.

Simply having one bad sexual experience where a partner found something about you a bit of a turn-off, or told you they were getting bored in the bedroom, or cheated on you, etc., can scar someone for ages if not for life.

Academy rule no. 19: Any student that's had a bad sexual experience should reassure themselves that by far the majority of people have had similar experiences. You're not alone and shouldn't let it affect future sexual relationships.

As with most of the advice in this book, the confidence and communication advice applies equally to men and women.

The common threads of sexual confidence

Here are a few of the most common areas affecting sexual confidence:

- ❂ A lack of sexual confidence often relates to how your partner treats you. If you think they have negative feelings about you in the bedroom – don't find you attractive, are bored with what you two do, etc. – it rocks your confidence.

Academy confidence tip: Always let your partner know how much you appreciate them generally and in the bedroom. If you can help grow each other's confidence it benefits your whole relationship as well as the sex.

◐ Having a partner that never praises or compliments you can affect your self-confidence. Receiving praise can have a tremendous effect on a person's confidence.

Academy confidence tip: Think of giving compliments and praise as like watering a flower – it will flourish and grow. It never hurts – and always helps – to tell someone you love them, find them sexy, that they're looking good, and so on.

◐ Many times partners don't realise they neglect to praise or compliment the person they supposedly love more than anything in the world. This usually reflects the way people have been treated within their families – perhaps their families never gave praise or compliments.

Academy confidence tip: It might be your responsibility to give your partner a nudge to let them know that you need more obvious signs of their appreciation. It helps you grow your confidence if you learn to ask for such praise and appreciation.

◐ It's a fact that sexual confidence is definitely intertwined with general confidence. This means that on a day-to-day level people need to value themselves. There's nothing wrong with talking yourself up and reminding yourself of your good points. Definitely challenge any negative voice – the devil on your shoulder – that criticises you. It doesn't make you vain or selfish to tell yourself you're pretty damn good at something or pretty hot in bed.

Academy confidence tip: When the timing feels right 'sex up' your compliments – tell your partner how hot you find her breasts or how gorgeous his bum cheeks are. You can even go so far as to tell her it feels like heaven being inside her. Or tell him you love his hard throbbing cock inside you.

Academy study tip: Think-in-ink and put pen to paper; write a list of all your good qualities. Read this list every day.

Lesson 2: Building body confidence

One area that profoundly affects sexual confidence for practically every woman – and many men – is body image. I once conducted a large study on body image and found the average woman has incredibly low levels of body confidence.

The way we feel about ourselves has much to do with the shape, size and weight of our body. We place far too much emphasis on what we view as an ideal, sexy body for both men and women. Most of us simply can't live up to these ideals.

The way you feel about your body definitely affects your sexual confidence. Unfortunately it can have a real negative effect on whether or not you feel confident enough to give yourself some self-pleasure – to masturbate. Someone who thinks they have an ugly or overweight body often doesn't want to touch themselves. And what did the Professor of Pleasure teach you about self-pleasure? It's crucial to learning what gets you off – and what turns you off.

Academy body confidence tips

Let's get your body hang-ups banished from your bedroom:

◗ If you have any issues pleasuring yourself because you think your body is unattractive, overweight and/or misshapen then give yourself 'permission' to get to know your body. Remind yourself it's completely natural to touch yourself.

◗ Think back to where these feelings originated – maybe your parents told you off when they caught you touching yourself in your bedroom. Allow your rational mind to take charge over negative feelings from childhood about self-pleasure. It's no one's business what you do to yourself in private.

◗ Give yourself daily reminders of your sexiest attribute – maybe you have a naughty smile or cheeky glint in your eye. Value these special little things about yourself.

◗ Every day find a quiet place, close your eyes and relax while visualising yourself as a sex goddess or sex god. Keep this image in mind and use lots of detail to make it spring to life. Hang onto it – you can be that god or goddess!

◗ Increasing body confidence takes practice so spoil yourself – get something sexy to wear and strut around in it at home. At first you'll feel silly but gradually you will think, 'Hmmm, I don't look so bad after all!'

◗ Next practise slipping out of your clothes slowly and confidently in front of a mirror. You'll soon feel confident getting out of your sexy gear when you're with your partner.

◗ With all the practice in the world you still might end up getting a zip stuck when your partner is lying on the bed waiting for you – learn to laugh at such moments!

◗ When it comes to choosing the things to wear around your partner choose outfits that accentuate your good attributes.

Be proud to flaunt those – whether it's your breasts, bottom, legs, shoulders, etc. We all have one good attribute.

◐ If possible transform your best attribute into an erogenous zone – flaunt it so that your partner has easy access to caress and kiss it.

◐ So you think you're the only one with body issues? Think again – that new lover or long-term partner probably has as many body image issues as you do.

◐ Just as you should with general negative thoughts, learn to suppress negative thoughts about your body. Tell yourself things like nobody's perfect, no one who cares about you is going to worry about lumps and bumps, etc. You can spend your life wishing you had a smaller bum or bigger breasts or you can spend your time thinking about more important things.

◐ Try training your mind to feel sexier by weaving sexiness into your daily life; try wearing nice, silky underwear to work.

◐ Continue such mind-training by doing things like running your hands over your erogenous zones – not as in masturbation but just feel how nice your skin is to touch. This helps your general sensuality.

◐ Again, I'm going to remind you that sexual partners rarely pay as much attention to our real or imagined lumps and bumps. They usually get an eyeful of what they like and ignore the rest. If they're into you they're far more forgiving of imperfections.

◐ Most important of all focus on yourself as a whole person – you're far more than your physical attributes. Think about what you'd tell a best friend or loved one if they fretted over their body – that they were worth so much more and it didn't matter. Tell yourself that too.

When your partner has body image issues

When you're with someone with body image issues it can be a real worry. If you care about them you don't want them to feel bad about their body. And you can always sense that it's going to affect your sex life. In a long-term relationship this often happens after having a baby, when the woman lacks confidence in her post-baby body. Try these strategies:

- ◑ Appreciate yourself for having noticed your partner's struggles – the fact you're so in tune with their deeper anxieties is a great starting point.

- ◑ If you think your partner is suffering serious body image issues than suggest taking sex off the agenda while you two try different ways to boost their confidence.

- ◑ Definitely take a broad-brush approach and look at ways generally to boost their confidence – setting goals, getting new training in a job, etc. All these things have positive spinoffs for specific areas related to confidence like body image.

- ◑ Give them lots of genuine praise and compliments. Even if they have low body image it doesn't mean their bullshit radar is switched off and they'll know if you're being fake.

- ◑ Have a fun shopping afternoon together and encourage her to get one of those free fashion or makeup makeovers many department stores offer.

- ◑ Sometimes something as simple as a new haircut and makeup can give a woman with body image issues a lift.

- ◑ Crank up the romance with little daily romantic gestures to boost their confidence. It only takes little things like love notes, candlelit dinners, buying a romantic CD, etc., but these will make your partner feel good about themselves.

◐ Let your partner who lacks body confidence know it'd turn you on to be able to pleasure him or her. Really give them loads of detail of what you'd like to do, but be tactful and dim the lights when you get them in bed until their body image is boosted.

Academy sex tip: Get sexy and play a hot little game where you say you'll strut across the bedroom in your pants and dare her to do the same. It can be loads of fun mucking about with little games – and you might agree that she just sits in an easy chair or on the bed in her sexy knickers rather than having to flaunt herself.

Lesson 3: Top tips to lose inhibitions

Some crucial steps towards losing your sexual inhibitions:

◐ Begin at the beginning and rekindle your childhood confidence by having a giggle and doing something childish together. You could go to a theme park or fun fair together and lose your grown-up stresses and strains. Shrieking with delight and having a giggle helps you break free of adult anxieties and responsibilities.

◐ Take advantage of good weather – if the sun's out find a beauty spot where you can strip off to your underwear for a sexy picnic or even go skinny-dipping in the local lake. (Mind you, ONLY if it's a swimming lake – never risk swimming in unknown waters.) The lush, rushing water swirling around your body makes you feel so good you shed your inhibitions.

◐ Do something that takes you out of your comfort zone – dump going to your exercise class and instead go to a stripping or lap-dancing lesson. There's no rule saying you'll have to put on a performance for your partner if you take one of these lessons, but it can really help you lose body inhibitions. And if you get your confidence high enough you can put on a hot show for him. Work up a fantasy scenario around this theme – you're a stripper in a club and he's a handsome client that asks you for extras, etc.

◐ Get creative and think about who inspires you because of their sexiness or attractiveness. It might be a Hollywood star or a rock god – turn them into your private mascot, inspiring you to be the most confident and sexy you can be. Visualise their confidence when you see them strut down the red carpet looking like they own the place. Hold this mental image and grab yourself some of their confidence.

◐ Set your pulses racing and watch a scary movie together. Research finds that getting lost in the excitement and adventure of a thriller helps people dump their own worries.

◐ Devise your own super hot 'signature sex technique' – this involves taking a sex technique you already do well and making it even better. This can really help you lose inhibitions since you feel confident doing your signature technique. What is it you enjoy or do well when it comes to sex? Let's say you're great at kissing and also pretty good at giving oral sex. Why not devise your very own oral kissing technique that uses your kissing prowess. For instance, think about the Eastern 'swirl and poke' kiss. You could devise a signature sex technique that uses that kiss by applying the kissing technique to his penis while giving him oral sex. When he's gasping with pleasure you'll throw your inhibitions to the wind and enjoy sex so much more.

◐ Think about your wider environment and making it more sensual. You can set up a 'love zone' in your bedroom where you know everything's to hand for creating a lovely mood.

Keep everything you need to hand, from sensual-smelling candles and matches to mood music CDs and some sexy things to throw on. Knowing you won't have to rush around looking for that CD to put on when you're both feeling frisky will make you feel much more confident.

◐ Lighten up a bit and try to develop a fun and carefree attitude about sex. This new attitude will spread to your partner and make you both more likely to shed inhibitions. It helps build trust between you so it doesn't seem like the end of the world if a new sex technique or position doesn't work out.

◐ Be prepared to take a technique you do well to a more daring level. Let's say he likes it if you squeeze and smack his bottom while he's on top of you in missionary position. Why not use one of your new sex toys (remember your homework from the last Lecture Series – buy one) and slip it between his bum cheeks to stimulate his anal area.

◐ Tease, tease and finally please your partner. Don't forget how before-play can start building during the day to become foreplay later on. Get on the phone and talk dirty to build the anticipation. A lesson on talking dirty is coming soon – it definitely helps shed your inhibitions to unleash your dirtier side.

◐ Turn the ordinary into the extraordinary – if you had a good night's sleep suggest having a leisurely breakfast in bed. Once you're fuelled with a lovely breakfast you may just slip into having some lazy morning sex.

◐ An inhibited partner might find that a little fantasy role-play helps them shed inhibitions and gain sexual confidence. There's lots coming up on fantasy and role-play in Lecture Series 7 – definitely coax them into letting go a bit with some fantasy chat. They can pretend to be someone completely different in this context.

❶ Be aware if you're using alcohol to shed your inhibitions. There's nothing wrong with a drink or two for getting in the mood, but there's a lot wrong when you can't have sex when you're sober. When sober begin with some flirting and see if you can move it on to full sex if you two are in the habit of only having sex after a few drinks.

Academy fact: Those who drink to excess are far more likely to experience erectile dysfunction.

Other key aspects to sexual confidence

Spare their blushes

It helps to develop your sexual confidence by knowing what you like and don't like. When you're confident enough to say no to something you don't like in bed then you know you've reached a pretty good level of confidence. It's often a lack of confidence behind people feeling they can't say no to something in bed.

When you love a partner, yet don't have much confidence, it can be hard to say no, particularly if they haven't picked up on your resistance. Not only do you not want to hurt their feelings but also you don't want to embarrass them. So you keep quiet and say yes to something you don't want to do. It's crucial that you learn to express how you really feel, using the communication tips coming in a moment.

Keeping up with the Joneses

Another aspect to sexual confidence is feeling that everyone else is swinging from the chandeliers. Making the assumption that others have far more sex than they do is a common mistake. Too many people buy into the myth that advertisers try and sell us – that everyone is sexed-up and at it all the time. That's simply not true!

Many people confide in me that their best friend is always having mind-blowing sex. I always challenge this by saying it's a fact that many people lie about and exaggerate their sex lives. Develop enough self-confidence to believe that what you do with a partner is what counts – not what someone else is getting up to between the sheets.

Academy motto: Each to their own! This means never having to worry about what other people do in bed. All that should concern you is your own needs, desires and sex drive.

Lesson 4: Ask and tell – boudoir communication

If you've paid attention in lessons your body confidence should be boosted by now. It's time to turn our attention to improving communication skills in the bedroom, particularly as one study found only 23 per cent of couples say they communicate well in the bedroom. That's less than a quarter – far too low a proportion.

I'm sure most people think of communication as the spoken word or conversation. Yes, the human voice is incredibly powerful – it can move you, persuade you and take you to all sorts of emotional levels. It can be anything from harsh to seductive and all points in between.

However, there are a number of key ways to communicate when it comes to sex. And let's not forget that communication is a two-way street: you want to communicate your needs to a partner and they want to communicate their needs to you. It can be so tricky. Just think how easy it is to get crossed wires in practically any relationship – within families, between friends, at work with colleagues. When it comes to sexual relationships the emotions underlying what you're trying to communicate are even more powerful and there's even more room for misunderstanding.

Because of this, many people end up treating sexual communication as always being something that's very serious. Yes, of course it's important and serious, but you don't have to have a sense of humour malfunction over bedroom communication.

Academy rule no. 20: All students must learn to ask for what they want in bed.

Let's go through the different levels of communication in what I see as a logical order.

Sexual communication without words

If you're in bed with someone then you've obviously got past the initial hurdles of deciding whether or not you're attracted to each other, hooking up and actually slipping between the sheets. So far, so good with your communication – well, at least on the whole. Many end up in bed with someone they're not so sure they want to be there with!

That aside, say you've got past the initial hurdles and you're happy to land up in the middle of foreplay with someone. Or you're in a long-term relationship but you'd like to change some of the things you do together in bed.

As talking to someone can seem positively daunting when wanting to try something new, change something you're doing or make sure you never do something again, let's begin with non-verbal communication. How do you do this? You lead by your behaviour.

'Sex-talk' that doesn't require speaking

You've already learned about the importance of body language in seduction in the second Lecture Series. But how do you use it to express your sexual needs when you don't want to ask for something? You use the little sex sounds that everyone makes during foreplay and lovemaking to communicate what's working well and what isn't.

Some people are embarrassed by these noises and try to stifle them, ending up as a silent sex partner. But you can put these sex sounds to good use for sexual communication. They can give your partner crucial signals about what's working for you with sighs, moans and groans.

Let's say they're kissing you in a way that feels really good – if you moan pleasurably they'll pick up that cue to continue. If they're touching your genitals in a way that feels fantastic then you can let out some sighs encouraging them to do more. So even if they're enjoying the moment they'll still be aware of such noises. Obviously you listen for their noises and are guided by them too. This is terribly important in sexual communication.

'Sex-talk' through some moves

Either alongside these noises – or instead of them – you can show your partner what's working or what you want more of through your behaviour. Even a new partner will pick up on you turning your body towards them as they touch you in a particular way and realise that you want more of that. If they're stroking your lower abdomen gently and you'd like them to touch you between your thighs, they'll notice if you open your thighs.

It's amazing how much information we can convey through such little moves. Although I do believe you shouldn't go to bed with someone before you can actually speak to them about sex, I know how many couples land up in bed before that point. And these techniques are perfect to show what's feeling good.

Definitely use clear facial expressions to show your partner how much you're enjoying something like foreplay. Even in the middle of foreplay they'll pick up on that smile of pleasure.

'Sex-talk' with your hands

Just as your sex-sounds can communicate so much to the person you're in bed with, so too can your fingers. Let them do the talking and convey a message to your partner about what you like or dislike. Try these tips:

- Take their finger and suck and lick it with the type of pressure you'd like them to use with their fingertips on your nipples, for example. Once you've stopped sucking/licking their fingertips, move their moist finger to your nipple and start swirling it around with the same pressure you've just used to suck it with.

- Take their hand and move it to where you'd like more stimulation. Let's say they've been stroking your stomach and you'd like them to move on to your pubic mound. You can place your hand on top of theirs and move it down a bit – they'll get the message.

- You can also keep your hand on top of theirs for a while and gently guide it back and forth in the way you'd like them to continue moving it once you release their hand.

- Give them your hand so that they can move it across their inner thighs or penis, for example, the way they want to be touched.

- You might have had lots of sex together but sometimes you want different sensations. Be confident enough to guide them into the 'what would do it for you' zone at that particular time. Moving your body against theirs in another way or into another position is a good way of doing this.

◐ Think back to something they told you about sex that turns them on. Simply start doing that for them and you might find that being sexually generous in this way makes them try harder to meet your needs.

◐ Get creative when you let your fingers do some of the 'talking' and do something like slipping a vibrator between you two for new sensations during thrusting.

These key steps can be done without speaking a word!

Get the talking started

We've all been there: you've put your foot in it and regret what you said to a lover. Even if we didn't mean to we might've hurt their feelings, turned them off, got a reaction we didn't expect, etc. If only we could build up our ability to communicate rather than shy away from it. This is particularly true when it comes to bedroom matters. Many people have told me in confidence the sort of things they haven't talked about with the person they should be talking about them with – their partner.

Having seduced your partner into doing what you want using your sex noises in communication, it's time to start using real sex-talk. One reason people feel anxious about talking about sex (or talking *during* sex) is that they don't feel they're very sexy and they think their voice is going to betray their nerves and anxiety. Let's begin with building your communication confidence before you're with your lover.

Time to talk

There are times when non-verbal communication won't work

and you have to say what you want. All students should be aware that it's equally about *what* you say and *how* you say it.

Here are the Academy rules for saying what needs to be said between the sheets:

- ◐ Don't ever use a critical tone of voice. And be aware that even if you think you're not sounding critical it may come across that way, depending on the sensitivity of what you're raising. So soften and lower your tone of voice – shrill, high tones are definite a turn-off and they probably won't listen.

- ◐ Definitely try to sound confident as this lets your partner know that you think things are positive and good between you. An anxious/nervous tone of voice gives the opposite message.

- ◐ Don't gabble excitedly about some new sex toy you've bought for example – no matter how excited you are about having fun with it later. It's not a turn-on, so steady your voice and they may respond positively.

- ◐ Slow down your natural pace so they can hear what you have to say first time around and not have to ask you to repeat yourself.

- ◐ If it's something you want them to do to you, add a sensual tone to your voice.

- ◐ Use the pretence of playing a little sex game to introduce a new tip, trick or technique. For instance, show your partner some dice, suggesting that you take turns rolling them. Each number represents a new sex technique to try. Make sure you suggest techniques you want to try to be represented by each number.

- ◐ Likewise, if it's something you want them to stop doing, always begin with a positive suggestion for something they can do instead. For instance, if you don't like the way they're kissing you behind your ear simply tell them you'd love it if they'd start kissing your breasts.

◐ If you're feeling particularly nervous you can always take a few moments to relax and visualise having this conversation. Have your visualisation end on a positive note. Research shows such techniques can give you a more positive vibe.

◐ If you're getting to know a new partner or are in a long-term relationship, choose your words bearing in mind how this person expresses him or herself and how you can appeal to that style of communication.

◐ Always reflect to your partner what you think they might be thinking. If you think they want to try something new why not say something like, 'I've been wondering if you wanted to try some new things in the bedroom.' It sounds positive and shows you want information.

◐ Don't imply that everything you're doing in bed right now is boring just because you want to try something new.

◐ You might be quite right that your partner always wants to do the same thing. But accusing them of that isn't helpful – even if true.

◐ Choose your moment wisely if it's anything that might be taken as a criticism. Definitely choose a time when you're both relaxed.

◐ Depending on what it is, you might want to chat to them outside of the bedroom – if it's a sensitive conversation you don't want the bedroom to become associated with difficult conversations.

Academy motto: **Speak and you shall get answers**

A few extra considerations

○ If your partner's a particularly sensitive person and might take practically anything as criticism then definitely run through in your mind what you're going to say beforehand. Imagine how it might sound to them.

○ It's a good idea to actually say it aloud to yourself – you can feel the impact of your spoken words.

○ Remember that even if it's a difficult issue, if you come across confidently it'll sound far less of a criticism.

○ Keep in mind that even if you're asking for them to try a hot new sex technique they might take it as a criticism, so have reassurance ready.

○ If you're trying to get them to try something new try turning it into some sexy banter – often a bit of fantasy chat will help. Maybe they've resisted being tied up or tying you up and you're dying to try this – you can tease them with your dressing-gown sash, saying you'd love it if they'd bind your wrists together with it, turning you into their sex slave.

○ If it's a conversation about the frequency of sex – let's say you want more sex – don't make it into a criticism. Turn it into a positive, saying how much you love the sex you're having and so quite naturally want more.

○ If you want a partner to stop doing something – let's say you don't like the way he spanks your bottom during sex – then say, 'I know it's quite sexy when you spank me but it also distracts me from reaching climax.' You can make your point without any hurt feelings.

○ Here's the word 'creative' again – get creative and use special events like birthdays, anniversaries, etc., to suggest something special to try. Put like this it seems like you only want to add special pleasure to the celebrations.

❍ Use this Lecture Series to show your partner new things. While relaxed and chatting, suggest browsing through it together. Make it fun – suggest opening the book to a random page and trying a suggestion from it.

❍ Spoil yourselves and take an occasional 'refresher' weekend together – a great excuse to try a new tip, trick or technique without having to make a big point of it. New surroundings put people in the mood to do new things.

❍ You can boost your chances of trying something new by telling them you'd find it a massive turn-on doing something new to them to give them pleasure. How could they resist an offer like that?

Academy rule no. 21: One study found that merely saying those three little words 'I love you' put people in the mood for more sex. So if you're in a relationship, say it more frequently.

Academy suggestion: Why not make asking what you'd like into a bit of foreplay? You can do this when you're cuddled up by saying something like: 'Let's take turns describing one place we'd like to be kissed, stroked or touched.' You can also suggest closing your eyes while you take turns because it can be a turn-on listening to the descriptions of what you'd each like touched or kissed.

Lesson 5: Red, hot and dirty

Talking dirty is popular with many couples and can spice things up. But if you've never tried dirty talk with a new partner don't freak them out by saying something like 'Open those hot, juicy pussy lips because super-cock's coming in!'

Straightforward sexual etiquette will guarantee that talking dirty can become part of your sex life, so use these suggestions:

- ◐ If you're with a new partner suggest it in a sexy way – something like 'Do you mind if I use a little dirty talk?'
- ◐ Use a sensual – rather than an over-sexed – tone of voice and you'll probably get further.
- ◐ As with so many things, practising saying dirty words on your own can be really helpful.
- ◐ Gauge their reaction before starting any dirty talk – you should be able to tell if they're too embarrassed or actually quite like the idea.
- ◐ A great starting point can be giving each other risqué or sexy nicknames. He might love it if you call him 'big boy' and she might love it if you call her 'sexy vixen'. And using such naughty nicknames gives you a sexy, private bond.
- ◐ And if you feel like it, be playful and give your own bits sexy nicknames – give your penis a nickname like 'The Champion' and tell her the Champion's feeling 'very horny'.
- ◐ Begin with something not too 'red, hot and Dutch' – keep it light and a bit more flirty than dirty.
- ◐ Build both of your confidence to say something naughty to each other by both writing out a list of naughty words you'd like each other to say. Then take turns reading through each list – in a seductive voice, mind you.
- ◐ Definitely don't unleash a slew of dirty talk like you're a porn star in action – instead, once you've got permission, use it occasionally.
- ◐ Even with red-hot chat you can be positive in the things you say. Never use it as a cover to be critical of your partner. (Although the exception to this might be if you're both up

for some S&M and give each other permission to be called
dirty names, etc.)

- ◐ Typical of the Academy advice that applies to so many situations: practice makes perfect.
- ◐ Encourage your partner to practise trying out dirty talk in a fun way. There's no reason you can't have a giggle about it.
- ◐ If you suddenly come out with something like 'I want to ride you like a stallion!' and it sounds funny then laugh at it.
- ◐ Definitely try out some of your dirty talk on the phone – if you can turn each other on that way then you're making progress. Take your time, lie back and describe to each other what you're touching and how you're doing it. Use plenty of delicious detail. He'll be all ears if she describes to him exactly how she's touching and tweaking her nipples.

Let your fingers do the walking as you do the sexy talking
As you're touching, stroking and caressing each other you can whisper all these new things you've been saying to each other to heighten your pleasure. Combining foreplay with word-play can really keep things hot between you. Imagine stroking your partner's inner thigh, gently nudging their vagina and telling them how much you love their 'sweet pussy'. I think you get the picture.

Lesson 6: When the going gets tough
There are times when you can hint at wanting to change something in your sex life – or even try to be more direct – and it just doesn't work. Sometimes a partner won't want to hear what you're hinting at. They might be in denial about the state of your sex life. And that means you have to become more frank with them.

For instance, I've had plenty of women confide to me that

their partner is simply too rough or clumsy and they've tried everything to hint about changing this. No one wants to be hurt in bed even accidentally – unless they're into S&M.

Here are tips to 'talk tough' without making things worse

- ☉ Turn things around and put the ball in their court by raising the issue you want to discuss and finding out how they feel about it. Not only does this show you respect their point of view and want to sound them out, but they might have a take on it that you hadn't thought of and that could kick-start a whole different conversation.

- ☉ That said, never go into such conversations expecting the worst – that they'll be upset or you'll both be embarrassed. It may not happen that way at all.

- ☉ Be direct (but tactful) as you can lose someone's attention when beating around the bush.

- ☉ Resist making any sweeping generalisations that this particular issue ALWAYS happens. For instance, you might be raising the issue of a man ejaculating too quickly leaving you high and dry. Saying that this always happens – and you need to sort it out – can be incredibly daunting for the man on the receiving end. Hopefully there's been an occasion where he hasn't ejaculated too quickly. And even if there hasn't you need to give someone in this situation a bit of hope.

- ☉ After beginning the conversation, try and make it a back-and-forth style of conversation rather than you just going on and on about this 'thing' that's been troubling you in the bedroom. It's all too easy for the more dominant partner to take over such conversations and it may never get sorted out.

- ☉ Never jump the gun on a suggestion your partner might make to change or solve the issue. Take time and suggest thinking around their suggestion. It might be worth the effort as they may have a good point.

◐ Always create a sense that you two are working on this together so that any discussion doesn't become a 'you versus me' type of situation. You're far less likely to find a solution when you feel pitted against each other.

◐ Sometimes it's better to underestimate the 'issue'. And if you're concerned your partner is not happy with sex it's always better not to exaggerate your worries until you really know what's going on. The key is not blowing up issues into something bigger.

◐ Keep checking on what they think about what you're discussing. For example, pause and ask, 'Do you think so, too?'

◐ Obviously if it comes to something they're doing in bed that causes you physical or emotional pain, just tell them.

◐ When all else fails, never be frightened of telling your partner that you're lost for words. They may just be able to help you find the words to express yourself.

◐ If it's the issue of having safer sex that's causing you embarrassment or worry – get over it. Your sexual health is far more important than your embarrassment.

Academy fact: You – or a partner – are not mind-readers. We assume we know what's on someone's mind but we can be so wrong. With a long-standing partner in particular it's easy to think you know what they like, you know when they're in the mood or not, or when they want to talk about something. But that's not always the case. Better to ask than to guess.

Academy pointers for long-term relationships: In some ways it's probably even more important to keep quality communication going when in a committed relationship. During the golden honeymoon phase things are so hot, your sexual chemistry is so intense, that you might ignore certain things that require more communication. You get by on the animal passion between you but over time that isn't enough.

Try and build honesty and good sound communication between you on a daily basis. Don't sweep things under the carpet – have the courage to face them as they arise. And keep some subtle sexiness between you, like throwing in the occasional flirty – if not dirty – word/phrase when you're chatting.

Academy sexy-chat tip: Have fun with some sexy chat and make them guess what technique you're describing when you say: 'It involves some luscious cream, my fingertips and a special place on your body!'

When things get difficult

Sometimes with the best will in the world – plus the best communication techniques – anger builds up anyway on one or both sides. Because certain issues – including sexual ones – strike right at the heart of the way we feel about ourselves, it's understandable that powerful feelings can emerge.

Sometimes there is a power struggle going on in a relationship and it comes out in the bedroom. Or it's easy to use sex as a bargaining chip – withdrawing it if you're angry or hurt. This means difficult feelings around sex or other issues can seep into each other.

When it gets to this point a negative cycle develops. You can both end up feeling defensive and sometimes the first way to start fixing this is to draw a line under how you've been relating to each other recently. This might be the perfect time for a 'sex-free sabbatical' which can take the heat off the sexual side of things. This can make it easier to re-establish more loving feelings between you as things become simpler.

This is a good time to build in plenty of regular compliments and do each other little favours, both slowly building goodwill between you. Even leaving a loving note or sending a loving text will help. Try igniting a little fun again as things relax, and over a month or so see if that loving feeling comes back.

Once you both feel more loving communication return, your confidence will be boosted to share a full-on sexual relationship once more. If not, it might be advisable to try couples counselling.

Final words on communication

As Professor of Pleasure I don't want Academy students to be daunted by the 'C' word. Everyone can be forgiven mistakes when it comes to communication, like putting your foot in it or saying the wrong thing at the wrong time. You can always apologise and try harder next time.

It can be invaluable to establish a good sense of humour when it comes to mistakes of communication. Forgive your partner when they say the wrong thing and know they have. And encourage them to not feel it's the end of the world if a conversation has backfired.

It's easy to be scared of honest communication – it is daunting letting someone in, but it's worth it! Without communication we diminish the chances of a satisfying sex life and a full relationship. I began this Lecture Series by highlighting how intertwined communication and confidence are. They're both part of a step-by-step process. Sometimes it's one step forward and two steps back when it comes to two people in a sexual relationship.

Hopefully after putting all these tips into action you'll soon find your sexual confidence and communication skills are far superior to what they have been. You'll discover so many more possibilities when it comes to sex and the rest of your relationship – and hopefully you won't look back.

Lecture Series 5 Sex-amination

Circle the answer that you think is correct. Count up your number of A, B and C answers and then check the answer key below.

1/ *Are communication and confidence related to each other?*
   A/ *No, they're two different things*
   B/ *Sometimes*
   C/ *Yes, definitely*

2/ *If you're embarrassed about talking dirty what should you do to change that?*
   A/ *Just come out with a stream of rude words until you get used to saying them*
   B/ *Ask your partner for advice*
   C/ *Definitely practise on your own*

3/ *When should you have a sex-free time in your relationship?*
   A/ *Never, how can you make such a suggestion*
   B/ *If one of you is ill*
   C/ *It could be a very good thing to try when you're having problems*

4/ *Are you or your partner mind-readers?*
   A/ *Yes, I always know what my partner's thinking*
   B/ *I could take a good guess*
   C/ *No, we're not*

5/ Can you communicate about sex without using words?
   A/ No, of course not
   B/ Maybe, it might work
   C/ Yes, definitely

6/ If you have to talk about a sex issue what's the best way
   to start?
   A/ If it's that tricky sweep it under the carpet
   B/ Probably just get on with talking about it
   C/ Start on a positive note about something you enjoy together

7/ If your last partner liked 'talking dirty' does that mean your
   present partner will?
   A/ Yes, who wouldn't
   B/ They might like it
   C/ No, not necessarily – they're two different people

8/ Could there be any benefit from pretending you're a sex god or
   goddess?
   A/ I don't have to pretend, I am one
   B/ Maybe, but I'm a bit sceptical
   C/ Yes, to help build your sexual confidence

9/ Can you communicate sexual preferences with your hands and
   without words?
   A/ No, it's always better to use words
   B/ I'm not sure
   C/ Yes, you can show the sorts of things you'd like to try/do

10/ Can it be helpful to your sexual confidence to go to an adult shop
    with your partner?
    A/ No, it would be embarrassing

B/ It might be

C/ Yes, because you could have lots of fun

Number of As: _____

Number of Bs: _____

Number of Cs:

◑   Mainly As: Astoundingly poor

You're very closed-minded about how sexual confidence and communication works. If you don't become more aware and sensitive you'll have many issues in your sexual relationships.

◑   Mainly Bs: Better pay more attention in lectures

It might seem like hard work learning about communication and confidence instead of learning about sex tips and tricks, but at least part of you recognises it's necessary. It's time to fully accept just how important communication and confidence are to a satisfying sexual relationship.

◑   Mainly Cs: Spectacular! Could hardly do better

Well done: you understand that sensitivity and awareness are required when trying to change things in your sex life. You realise that people can communicate in so many different ways and that sexual confidence can be boosted in a variety of ways too.

Giving an Oral Presentation

Academy students should now be fully prepared for this Lecture Series all about oral sex techniques. Hot and satisfying oral sex takes some finesse, a willingness to please, good communication and good sound basic knowledge of sex techniques.

Lesson 1: Introduction to oral presentations

Before we get to the huge variety of tips and before you 'dive' on down there, here are a few important points.

Oral sex is amazing and research suggests many women find it easier to climax through oral sex rather than penetrative sex – this is an important fact. That's not to say that the majority of women prefer oral sex, but certainly many find it incredibly satisfying once they have the trust in their sexual partner to try it.

Many women find that some oral sex plus some penetrative sex equals the perfect sexual experience. It certainly gives an added dimension to your sex life.

Women aside, most men love receiving oral sex. At the Academy we discourage any selfishness and if you expect to receive it then you should expect to give it. I'm not suggesting for a minute that more men refuse to give oral sex than those women who refuse to give it. But I do hear from many women that their partners seem resistant to giving them oral sex.

Why do some people refuse to give oral sex? There are many reasons but three of the main ones revolve around fear. The first one is they worry they won't do it right. This includes the fear of asking what to do and showing their lack of knowledge about oral sex. But also there is simply fear of the unknown. The last Lecture Series will have offered plenty of advice for communicating about any sex technique, including oral sex. So you can rule out this fear as an excuse for not trying it.

The next main fear people have is that they won't like their partner's taste and they feel pretty freaked out about the whole idea of oral sex. They don't want to offend a partner by letting them know this is how they feel about it, so they often simply resist any hints to try oral sex. Many tips coming up to get around this particular fear.

Many find it so intimate that they fear doing it with someone unless they have established complete trust with them. Oral sex does go right to the heart of physical intimacy – you can't get more personal and intimate than staring at your partner's private parts! And it really worries many people, especially women – they don't want their genitals to be judged as ugly or unpleasant.

Many other feelings and attitudes towards oral sex revolve around anxiety of some sort. Some people get the message – probably from their parents but also their peers – that oral sex is dirty. These negative attitudes are difficult to break down.

One final point about attitudes towards oral sex: some people believe that oral sex is less important than full penetrative sex. So they figure oral sex is really part of foreplay. Considering how many women can successfully reach climax through oral, this simply isn't true. Many women would be very satisfied with just oral sex. Often it is men who feel that oral is just part of a whole package. It can be but it doesn't have to be. Couples need to communicate their feelings about this. The important thing about sex – any type of sex – is that you both get pleasure from it. It's up to you and your partner what you do.

Academy rule no. 22: Students should keep an open mind about oral sex pleasure. Some research suggests that around 50 per cent of people never even try it. Don't knock it until you've tried it.

Sadly, fears and worries about the intimacy of oral sex stop many people trying it. Sometimes it's best to throw caution to the wind, go with the heat of the moment and dive down there to sex-periment.

But fear not, there are so many tips and techniques in the following lessons that you'll be masters and mistresses of oral sex by the end of this Lecture Series. Before we come to these, let me give all students a quick reminder about safer sex. I must stress the importance of using safer sex techniques with oral sex. Many don't realise you can transmit STIs through mouth-to-genital sex, e.g., oral herpes can be transmitted to the genitals and vice versa.

He should put a condom on when he's receiving a blow job. And even in the heat of the moment you can surely find some cling film to put over her clitoris and vagina while he gives her oral pleasure. Ideally strong cling film or a dental dam is best – be sure to cover the entire vaginal area.

Academy warning: Make sure you don't rupture the condom, cling film or dental dam with your teeth as oral sex gets more vigorous when your partner gets near orgasm.

Let's get the oral party started

In Lecture Series 2 a huge array of kissing techniques were covered and equally with oral sex there are many different techniques to use. It doesn't just involve your lips and tongue but also touching with your fingers, and there's an array of special techniques to try. It's far more than just licking your partner's bits.

Of course in foreplay you might just enjoy a couple of minutes of oral – some licking and kissing and nibbling and then on to full sex. But never underestimate the variety of sensations you can give and receive by altering your technique slightly.

It's good manners to ask

Having covered communication in the last Lecture Series I'm going to repeat the message that it's good to ask when you're with a new partner if they want you to go down on them – rather than just diving down. During foreplay you can demonstrate interest in giving them oral by planting kisses down their abdomen. As you plant kisses you can murmur that you'd love to 'go down' on them.

Always start very gently and ask if the first sensations you're giving feel good. Everyone's different and one woman might like her clitoris gently flicked with the tip of your tongue while another woman might like to feel the flat of your tongue rubbing against her clitoral area.

It's the same with men – some are so sensitive that they just want a woman to gently massage the end of their penis with her lips. Others want a full-on suction action. Even a partner that wants a strong sensation would probably be shocked if you went down on them and started giving them a strong sucking or licking action straight away.

Lesson 2: Academy tips and techniques for going down on your partner

- Your tongue is a lovely big muscle so get it in shape with some exercise. Open your mouth and whirl it in a circular motion, flutter it around and generally loosen it. Do this daily so you're ready for tongue action any time. If you have to do presentations at work or any other public speaking this will help with that too.

- As there is probably going to be some hand action when giving oral sex – gripping the shaft of his penis while you suck his glans or spreading her labia while you lick and tease her clitoris – make sure your nails are filed and your hands are clean.

- So neither of you has to worry about anything but smelling fresh, definitely have a bath or shower beforehand. If you've been out clubbing together all night you definitely won't be smelling or tasting fresh.

- When you get in you can have a sexy shower together to get the foreplay started. Lovingly and sexily soap each other down.

- Mind you, it's important women don't over-use shower gels and soap because there is a delicate pH balance in the vagina.

- A woman should consult her doctor if she ends up with an irritation or unpleasant smell despite being 'clean'. This might be due to a vaginal pH imbalance.

- So your partner doesn't feel they're fighting their way through a pubic jungle, trim your pubic hair. It's easier to keep clean and smelling fresh with short pubes. And it's easier to receive great oral sex!

Academy tip: **Have fun with some sexy trimming and shaving. Only do this when sober – take turns shaving and trimming each other's pubic hair. You can use your fingers to stroke gently through their hair as you trim it. Use some fun sexy chat (as suggested in the last Lecture Series) and tease them a bit as you touch them. A top tip for shaving: try using hair conditioner with the razor rather than shaving foam since it might irritate the sensitive skin of that area.**

More Academy tips for making oral fantastic

- As taste is a concern for many partners why not smooth over his penis/her clitoral area some yummy chocolate sauce, fruit yoghurt or honey – any flavour you like that doesn't irritate their skin. You can lick it off a bit at a time as a compromise for giving full oral.
- Remember that the way you taste – his penis, her vagina – is affected by what you've eaten. Things like spicy and salty foods will alter the taste of your natural juices.
- Hopefully if you have any issues about oral sex and not liking the taste, once you're both clean and fresh and smothered in yummy-tasting things you'll enjoy it. You might even savour giving oral.

A few oral dos and don'ts

- Don't just lie there and take it if your partner's giving you really bad oral sex. Try this technique instead: ask them for a little more foreplay and while you're kissing think about how the way they kiss you might work to give you good oral. Say something about how much you love the way they kiss and you'd love it if they'd do the same down below.

◐ Most people enjoy oral sex that builds up from very gentle pressure to much stronger pressure to bring them to climax. That means the receiver should keep talking a bit – let them know if it needs to be softer or stronger.

◐ Don't go straight in with your tongue when giving oral sex to her for the first time. Most women prefer a man to start by using his lips only as the clitoris can be sensitive to little jabs of the tongue, for example. Simply kiss her genitals like you were kissing her lips.

◐ Do ASK for feedback as you continue giving oral. I know I've just said you should tell your partner which sensations feel best but you can't assume that's going to happen. If you're the 'giver' do keep getting that feedback.

◐ Do check out how your partner feels about you climaxing in their mouth. Many people have an issue with this. If you're using safer sex practices you wouldn't do this, but if you have both had full STI screens and aren't using safer sex methods check out how they feel about this.

◐ Particularly for men, if she's happy for you to ejaculate in her mouth do give her a warning when you reach that point.

◐ Don't be pressured into giving/receiving oral sex if it's not your thing. I know it's an Academy rule that you should keep open-minded but sometimes there's no changing this.

◐ Do be prepared to compromise and simply kiss around their abdomen, pubic mound and inner thighs while you stroke their genitals. You might be perfectly happy giving them a climax with a hand job while you're kissing the general area.

Lesson 3: Advancing your level of oral technique

If you've had more than one sexual partner you'll know there is humdrum oral sex and there is mind-blowing oral. One partner might touch, lick, stroke, flick, kiss and suck you all over – turning you into their erotic feast and giving you a powerful orgasm. Another might go down on you, lick you a few times and that's your lot.

There's room for improvement for most people so here are some extra tips to maximise your technique.

Sex-periment with the following:

Licking – It's quite simple to give a nice basic, pleasurable sensation if you imagine you're licking a lollipop. This is a good place to start, especially with a new partner – just keep it gentle and try and find a nice rhythm.

For her: begin with little licks along her pubic bone. Then move downwards, licking around her clitoris, her outer and inner labia, and her introitus (the opening to her vagina).

For him: try licking gently upwards from the base of his shaft up to the tip of his glans. Or moving the other direction and gently lick down his inner thighs, around his testicles and down below them to his perineum.

Lapping – OK, you started by licking a little lollipop; now pretend you're lapping a luscious ice-cream cone! Lapping is simply a bigger version of licking. Think back to Lecture Series 2 and the kissing technique called the Sloppy Dog. Students will recall this is where your mouth goes slack and you lap with a completely relaxed tongue.

For her: a larger lap feels fabulous, beginning from her perineum and lapping right over her introitus, and then back and forth across her labia. Definitely use a lapping action across her pubic bone – it'll stimulate her clitoral arms.

For him: definitely use large lapping strokes around his testicles and again up and down his penis when he's erect.

Poking – As with the Eastern Swirl and Poke kiss, you can use a gentle poking action during oral sex. What you need to imagine is gently poking your tongue into his urethral opening at the tip of his penis, or around her clitoris and into her vagina. Think of this action as the way the tip of your tongue might gently poke into the creamy centre of a chocolate éclair.

For her: simply poke your tongue along the edges of her labia and into her vagina as if you were eating a yummy and delicate sponge cake and trying to get icing out from between the layers. Try using the poking action along her pubic mound and on either side of her clitoris – she needs to have confidence that you're not going to jab her clitoris, though! If you've got the confidence, do this along the perineum and anus with plastic dams or cling film in place.

For him: if he doesn't like a poking sensation in his urethra at the tip of his penis, you can use this action all along the ridge of his glans.

Sucking – A classic oral technique, your sucking action needs to be applied correctly. Try and picture sucking a long piece of spaghetti into your mouth. Imagine imitating this action and you've got it.

For her: Use this later in oral sex when she's highly aroused. Gently apply this sucking action to her clitoris – you might place your lips around her clitoral hood rather than pulling it back if she's sensitive. Try applying it on her inner labia, gently sucking for a few moments, then releasing and gently moving on her labia, pausing to suck for a while, releasing the pressure, etc.

For him: It's wrong to assume that all a man wants is the head of his penis sucked during oral sex. If truth be told, you should be careful sucking the head of his penis as it might feel too painful. What's the Academy rule? Always begin gently and let him guide how much sucking pressure he wants. This is a great action for taking one of his testicles in your mouth and sucking inwards gently.

Swirling – Visualise a lush, swirling whirlpool and try using your tongue this way. This is where tongue flexibility exercises come in handy.

For her: She'll love the sensation of your tongue swirling around her clitoral area and, if you spread her lips, then swirling inside her vagina.

For him: He'll love a swirling action with your tongue up his shaft, then around his glans. It's also a perfect technique for swirling around his testicles.

Kissing – Get a sensual action going with some loving kissing across their genitals. Plant loads of soft kisses across them – it's quite a tease if you don't kiss directly on her clitoris or the head of his penis.

For her: She'll love little kisses planted across her pubic mound, down her labia, and along her inner thighs. Relax your lips – remember: no tension – so it feels super sensual. There's no stiff upper lip when it comes to oral sex! If she likes lots of clitoral stimulation, plant a few kisses around her clitoris and then place your lips gently around her clitoris. You can now blow her mind if you start pulsating your lips.

For him: When it comes to oral kissing, men have very different likes and dislikes – some men will find it a slightly annoying sensation if you plant gentle kisses around their penis and testicles. The solution is to try different pressures of kisses with your lips and ask which he likes.

Flicking – Porn films have a lot of negative things to answer for, including showing men flicking their tongues quickly and firmly across a woman's clitoris. And it's the same with female porn stars doing these rough flicks across the end of a man's penis. By far the majority of people having real sex would find this too painful. Ignore the porn action and only flick gently – build up the pressure only after checking with them first.

For her: Try a very gentle flicking action up and down her labia and along her perineum to give her hot sensations.

For him: For something different, try a light, fast flicking action with your tongue to give him a thrill. Practice makes perfect, so do those tongue exercises mentioned above.

Rubbing – This is something most people don't think of doing: using a rubbing action with their lips as opposed to kissing or licking. Simply relax your lips and rub them back and forth across their genitals or in circular movements.

For her: She'll love a rubbing action across her clitoris if you begin gently and build the pressure. Try rubbing your lips down and around her labia. She might want to climax with a rubbing action so suggest she holds your head and grinds against your lips as she builds to climax.

For him: It'll feel fabulous if you rub very moist lips against the end of his penis. But they must be moist to slip and slide across his most sensitive areas.

Humming – This sounds a bit bonkers but feels fantastic and it doesn't matter if you can't sing a note! Wrap your lips gently around one area – her clitoris or labia, the head of his penis and testicles and start humming gently to give wonderful vibrations.

For her: Wrap your lips gently around one side of her labia and start humming, alternating this with a sucking action. Between the gentle vibrations of the humming and the suction of sucking she won't know what's hit her.

For him: Wrap your lips around his testicles and begin the humming. Again you can alternate this with sucking his testicles to give him loads of pleasure. When you have his testicles in your mouth move your fingers up and down his shaft, stroking it gently.

Go for gold – As you get to know your partner's likes and dislikes try moving between different techniques: first swirling, then some kissing, next try humming, add in rubbing and then some lapping. Your tongue will get a workout but they'll be thankful for it!

Lesson 4: Touching techniques to heighten oral pleasure

Academy motto: Get creative by combining techniques.

Some partners will simply want you to focus your oral skills on their most sensitive erogenous zones; they like to concentrate on those specific sensations. But other partners will love it if you add in some touching as you're sucking, kissing, licking, etc.

As you know from foreplay lessons, there are lots of touching techniques and you can apply these in different ways to heighten the oral sex experience you give your partner. To get the very best out of your Academy education I'd like to break things down into very practical and manageable tips – you need to add your creativity when sex-perimenting with them.

Here are some Academy touching-action tips to supplement your oral technique:

Stroking – With your index and middle fingers gently stroke her clitoral hood. You can either stroke it backwards towards her belly button, lifting the hood gently with every stroke, or lightly stroke downwards towards her labia, releasing your fingertips from her clitoral hood and then going back to the base of it nearer her pubic bone to begin the stroking action again. This is called 'stroking the mouse's nose'. Do this while you're kissing/licking her labia and vagina. You can use a stroking action on him while sucking on his glans. Use a rhythmic stroke at the base of his shaft or underneath his glans at the top of his shaft. He might like this sensation on his perineum too.

Rubbing – Think of rubbing as a smaller, subtler version of stroking. You can imagine this touching action by thinking of gently 'sanding' something with your index and middle fingers. The delicate, small movement feels heavenly on her clitoral hood while you're kissing or licking across her pubic mound or down in her vagina.

Twirling – Again, you need to use your imagination and think of this as twirling a piece of spaghetti between two fingertips. Try this action just around her clitoris – NOT on the clitoris! So you might 'twirl' some of the flesh across her pubic mound while you nuzzle, kiss or lick her clitoris.

Pinching – Always start carefully when you're pinching your partner's fleshy areas, but this is a perfect touching technique to use while giving oral sex. You could gently pinch his perineum and bottom while sucking him. If you can reach then why not gently pinch and tweak her nipples while giving her oral – two very different sensations can be explosive.

Drumming – This is a lovely and unique sensation. Most people enjoy a light 'drumming' across their pubic bone. It's surprising how it can ignite all the nerves of her clitoris when you drum across her pubic mound. Try drumming up around the base of his shaft while sucking his glans. Imagine this action as mimicking the fall of little raindrops across your lover's skin.

Circular massage – You can apply your thumb, index and middle fingers to their skin with this delicate circular massaging action. Circle the skin on his perineum or her labia while giving direct oral sex. Such circular massage increases the blood flow to these areas, enhancing their sensations.

Taking touch to another level
For an explosive oral experience try some of the following techniques on her. She should be aroused and well lubricated when trying fingering techniques.

Pelvic rub – This is a great technique used when generally kissing her pelvic area and you want her to become more aroused. Using a couple of your fingers, gently rub the area a few centimetres below her belly button. If you do this even for a few minutes while licking or kissing her it'll stimulate the whole area.

The stir – You definitely want it 'stirred not shaken'. Hold your index and middle fingers together and insert them slightly into her vagina. Once inside simply hold them there, keeping your fingers still while she relaxes her vaginal muscles. After a moment start making a 'stirring' motion with them. This can stimulate her G-spot – if she feels she has one – while you kiss around her clitoral region. Even if she doesn't think she has a G-spot, it'll stimulate her vaginal walls – an often-neglected erogenous zone.

The grip – Shape your thumb and four fingers into a C-shape by nearly bringing them together. Now insert your thumb into her vagina allowing your four fingers to rest across her clitoral region. Begin gently rotating your thumb inside her while your four fingertips apply a little bit of pressure on her pubic mound.

Come on over – Try this for X-rated stimulation while giving her oral sex. This technique stimulates the G-spot area. Imagine your palm is facing upwards and your index and middle fingers are forming a 'come on over here' gesture. Moving downwards from her pubic mound, slip the two fingers slowly into her vagina – your fingertips should reach her G-spot. Then start a gentle stroking motion against this region as you lap around her clitoris for a double whammy.

The V sign! – This feels fantastic and can get her aroused before you give her oral sex. Imagine your index and middle fingers forming a V shape. Moving downwards from her belly button, slip these two fingers either side over her pubic mound down on to her labia – one finger on each of her labium. With a very small back-and-forth action you gently stimulate the pubic mound, clitoris and clitoral arms. After a few minutes of this she should be ready for you to start oral pleasure.

Labial massage – Do this while crouching between her legs, maybe crouching at the end of the bed with her hips pulled towards you. With your index and middle fingers and thumbs gently massage down one side of her outer labia – and then up the other. When you come to her clitoris gently circle it with one of your fingertips. Think of this action as how you'd gently knead bread dough. Definitely lubricate your fingers and always be gentle. Obviously don't pull on her labia – simply knead/massage them.

The handful – Again kneeling between her open legs, use this technique to drive her crazy. This technique massages her inner thighs, labia and vagina. Keep your fingers together and have your hands lightly cupped. Using a gentle action alternate moving your left and right hands up and down, starting at her pubic bone, then down over her labia and inner thighs. Gentle but large sweeping movements are ideal. Your hands will pass each other in opposite directions as they move up and down over her. There has to be a lot of trust as she needs to spread her legs wide for this to feel good.

The full four – This action uses all four of your fingers which relax down and over her pubic bone. Now your fingertips will touch her introitus – remember that's the opening to her vagina. All four of your fingertips can stroke, rub and circular-massage this area. Once she's fully aroused slip one, two or even three fingers into her vagina.

The beak – Again he is kneeling between her legs and places his fingertips and thumb together forming a beak shape. He turns his hand and palm upwards while applying the beak – giving a gentle circular massage with the beak shape slipped just inside her vagina. He can give her oral pleasure around her clitoris while the beak gently massages her.

Rear pleasure – A great technique for him if he's a bottom lover. If you two have been getting super hot in the sitting room, try this. She kneels on the carpet and bends over the edge of the sofa, or, if in the bedroom, she bends over the bed. He kneels to her side/behind her and strokes her from behind, kissing her bum cheeks as he does so. He can also kiss her labia and introitus if she arches her pelvis backwards away from the sofa or bed. He can place his open hand (imagine he's about to shake hands with someone) and hold her perineum and labial area. He can then gently rock his cupped hand either in a back-and-forth or circular motion, stimulating this area.

Loving the pearl – She needs to be turned on before you use this technique. If she likes direct clitoral massage she'll like this. Begin by resting your thumb and index finger either side of her clitoris. Depending on her preference, either pull her clitoral hood very gently back towards her belly button or leave it in place. Next use delicate, small back-and-forth actions to stimulate her clitoris between your thumb and index finger. Now for the finale – while doing this, gently circle her clitoris with your tongue. Depending on her sensitivity, you can build up the pace and friction of your movements – ask for regular feedback from her on how it feels.

Academy tip: Coax her into allowing you to watch as she touches herself. This gives you loads more info about how she likes to be touched. She should get daring and while touching herself, taste her very own love juices. She gently touches and teases

her clitoris before dipping her finger into her vagina and then
sensuously licks her finger. Seriously hot viewing for him!

A few more super hot Academy techniques

◐ For a couple that knows each other's sexual history and
you both have the all-clear: use the extra saliva from your
mouth to lubricate her vagina or his penis. Ignore the porn
stars that spit on each other's genitals to lubricate them.
This is far more subtle – slip some of your saliva onto
your fingertips to massage in before continuing to give
oral sex.

◐ Crank it up a bit when giving her oral sex by gently sucking out some of her own love juices. Hold in your mouth
and then move up to kiss her mouth so you can allow some
droplets of her love juices to go into her mouth.

◐ Try the 'nose nuzzle' during oral pleasure. While you use
different lip and tongue techniques, also start nuzzling
your partner with your nose. He can nuzzle her pubic
mound while licking her vagina. She can nuzzle the base of
his shaft/testicles while licking that area.

◐ We know from the last Lecture Series how much fun talking
dirty can be, so use a little dirty talk to tell them how good
their love juices taste. And any other hot thing you want
to say!

Here are a few choice oral moves for him

Just as women love extra touching when they're receiving oral
sex, so too do men. Many of the various tongue, lip and finger
techniques that can be used on a woman can also be used on a
man. For instance, he might like to feel her fingertips running
across and stroking his abdomen as she licks and sucks his

penis. Even feeling a few simple strokes on his testicles while you're tonguing his shaft will give him a thrill.

The foreskin – Just as no woman wants her clitoral hood abruptly pulled back, men who have an intact foreskin feel the same – he doesn't want it wrenched back either. As you touch his foreskin when you give him oral sex, ask if he likes it moved up and down, or pulled back completely and held in place. Pulling back will give you great access for full oral but he might also like the sensation of you moving it up and down while you lick the end of his penis. Definitely treat his frenulum with care – you may recall from Lecture Series 1 that this is the ligament on the underside of his glans that holds the foreskin in place. It's very sensitive.

His shaft – Men differ in the type of touch they like on the shaft of their penis, especially when he's fully erect and you're exciting him with oral sex. Some men prefer you to keep your hand still while giving him oral sex so he doesn't get over-excited. Other men will want excitement with your hand moving on their shaft while you suck them. And others might like alternating sensations where for a time you hold their shaft firmly and you alternate that with stroking or squeezing (having checked out how tightly he wants you to squeeze).

The testicles, perineum and anal area – He may be desperate for you to stroke these areas while you give him oral sex. Some straight men worry a partner might assume they are gay if they ask for this type of stimulation. Others simply think their partner will be put off finishing a blow job if they ask to be touched there. As with any anal-play, he should be fresh and clean and you need to use safer sex practices if you want to safely lick and kiss his anal area. Cover the anal area with cling film or a dental dam to stop transmission of germs if you'd like to orally pleasure him there.

The juicer – This requires both of her hands: one at the base of his shaft and the other placed gently just below his glans on the upper shaft. Think about how you juice an orange to get an idea of this action. She gently rotates one hand back and forth and then begins rotating the other hand too. She should keep asking him for feedback as she builds up speed and the pressure of her grip. At the same time she sucks the end of his penis.

The double header – He'll also love this technique, done when he's erect. She wraps her left thumb and forefinger around the base of his shaft and her right thumb and forefinger above them. As she sucks, licks and flutters her tongue over the end of his penis she begins moving her fingers up and down – moving her two sets of fingertips to meet mid-shaft.

Next she gently moves her two sets of fingertips apart with one set moving down his shaft and the other set coming back up to meet her lips at the head of his penis. She can repeat this as frequently as he wants.

Pearl pleasure – Give him a different sensation using a plastic pearl/beaded necklace (not a real one!). She lubricates his shaft and now wraps them gently around it. With both hands she clasps his shaft and very gently wiggles the 'pearls' slightly up and down. While she jiggles the beads she can lick or suck his glans.

Academy tip: Why not suck on a mint so the minty freshness coats the inside of your mouth. Now when you start licking his penis or her vagina they will feel the tingly freshness of your mouth – it feels fantastic!

Lesson 5: Pole positions for oral sex

You now have many tips and techniques to give your partner oral pleasure. But to make the most of these you need to be comfortable in order to give the very best oral action. By far the majority of couples slip into standard oral sex positions. When she's giving him oral sex he usually lies on his back and she lies across his lower abdomen. When he gives her oral sex he tends to lie between her legs.

You can maximise your comfort so that you can give a lovely long oral sex session to your partner. When it comes to comfort, position is all-important. Just think how his neck will feel if he's been lying between her legs for twenty minutes (it might well take her around twenty minutes to climax) – it'll feel incredibly strained. Or if she's giving him a blow job for more than five or ten minutes she may end up with the classic 'Blower's Cramp' where her mouth feels like it's about to cramp up – not sexy or relaxing. And many women are too embarrassed to say that they need a break and suffer in silence.

Academy rule no. 23: Students should never suffer silently if they're uncomfortable during any type of sex!

As is true with any position during sex, a couple should feel confident to move into another position to carry on, in this case, to continue giving more oral sex. Definitely keep to hand lots of cosy cushions to help keep you comfortable during sex. Particularly for oral pleasure – for instance, she might need a cushion to lift her hips while he gives her oral. Or she might need a cushion to support her head as she gives a blow job.

Here are some sex-tra Academy recommendations

Full on – This is a classic oral sex position when he's giving her pleasure. She lies back and he lies between her legs. For variation or comfort she can simply open her legs up or wrap one or both of her legs over his shoulders or around his neck.

So that he can have better access to her clitoris and vagina she can use her fingertips to spread her labia. He can also slip his fingers in there to help hold open her labia. As her sexual tension builds she might find that she gets optimum pleasure by holding the back of his head to guide it. This position is great for his lip and tongue action, but because he's between her legs he can probably only use one hand to finger her with.

Across the bridge – In this position she lies with her legs apart and he rests sideways across her hips. He places one of his hands on her pubic bone – this way he can use it to gently pull upward on her lower abdomen. This movement lifts her clitoral hood, exposing her clitoris. His other hand is free to explore between her legs and finger her. His tongue action is sideways across her clitoris – he licks across it and it can give fantastic (but not irritating) sensations for women who are sensitive.

Down under – This gets more adventurous, with her lying on her back. He turns nearly 180 degrees so that his legs move up towards her head – his face is down near her abdomen. He can rest his head gently on her abdomen so he faces at her pelvic region. This can give her entirely new sensations with him licking gently downwards over her clitoris and towards her labia. This is another great option for a sensitive woman who can't take direct clitoral stimulation, as her clitoral hood remains in place. He can move so that his tongue reaches down further between her legs where he can lick her labia and even down as far as her perineum – that's why it's called 'Down Under'.

Raising the flower – This position is great for partners who are flexible. They begin with him kneeling between her legs as she lies on her back. He can be kneeling on the floor at the edge of the bed. Her bottom is near the edge of the bed. She raises her legs to rest her calves on his shoulders. He pulls her hips slightly off the bed so that her genitals come towards his mouth – her hips rise slightly upwards. He can keep one hand wrapped around her waist, steadying her while he licks, kisses and sucks her vagina and clitoris. If he can reach, he can use the other hand to stroke her abdomen or fondle her breasts. As he gets a full view of her, this position isn't for the shy woman.

69 – This is a classic position where both partners can have oral pleasure at the same time. There are a couple of variations on 69. In the first, one partner lies on their back and the other lies above – they are head-to-toe. The partner on top is supported by their hands and knees. This is a very sexy position – both of you can be stimulated at the same time and you have a good view of each other's genitals. Definitely tickle and tease their perineum for a little extra pleasure. The second is the **Lovers' Knot (oral)** – this position is a variation of 69. In this position both partners lie on their sides. Again they are head to toe facing each other. They pleasure each other at the same time.

Many couples find the Lover's Knot more comfortable than traditional 69 and end up using it exclusively. And it's great for easy caressing and teasing wherever your hands can reach while continuing to give oral sex (remember the vibrator tip for this position in previous lessons).

Worship the triangle – Another great position for women who have a sensitive clitoris (i.e. most women). She lies on her stomach with her pelvis arched slightly upwards as if she's in the 'lazy' Doggy-style position. Or she can lie on her side with her legs open and upper knee bent. He approaches her from behind towards her 'triangle' – the area formed by her thighs and buttocks. This position gives him access to kiss the many sensitive areas of her lower labia, buttocks, perineum and anus (don't forget safer sex here – use a dental dam or cling film). Perfect for people who want a bit more adventurous oral sex.

Sitting pretty – Let's get versatile. Imagine she's sitting on the edge of the bed, chair or sofa – this gives him good access when he kneels between her legs. She has great control over his head by clasping it between her hands. Most women will love to have their partner literally at their feet, which is why it's called 'sitting pretty'. For the dominant women it's a big turn-on being in control like this. Get creative with this in the kitchen or bathroom – he lifts her on to the counter-top for easy access.

Easy over (oral) – This position is for experienced partners with strength and flexibility. She perches on the back of an armchair or sofa and allows her head and upper back to slip down into the seat, as in the full sex position of the same name in Lecture Series 4. She is fully exposed, which means he has great access and can literally 'feast' on her. A bit daring and exciting for a couple who want something different.

Standing pleasure – Now she's really going to get dominant by standing over him with her legs apart, he kneels between them and below her. He can reach upwards to grasp her bottom which helps him control the oral pleasure he'll give her. She can steady herself against a wall or table. A couple can even try 'standing pleasure' in the shower. It feels fantastic with water cascading downwards as he gives her amazing tongue action.

Reach the peach – This is perfect for when a couple want to get naughty when he gives her oral. He lies on the bed on his back while she kneels above him. This way he's got good access to give her stimulation. She can pretty much control things by raising herself up and down above him just by moving her knees and thighs. This can be a bit of a sexy game where she teases and tempts him by keeping just out of reach from his lips. But later on they might want him to control things when she gets near climax – he can clasp his arms around her bottom, holding her tightly once she's ready to orgasm.

Direct clitoral stimulation – If you're with a new partner, ask if she likes direct clitoral stimulation. If she does, try this technique. He's between her legs and places his hand flat across her pubic bone and then pulls it gently upwards a centimetre or so towards her belly button. Her clitoral hood (prepuce) will be lifted, exposing her clitoris for his tongue action.

Academy warning: Everyone is different but the majority don't enjoy direct clitoral stimulation — unless they're super turned on. Make sure she's comfortable if you're going to experiment with moving her clitoral hood. Anyway, as she gets excited her clitoris gets engorged and might 'peep' out from under its hood.

Academy fact: Some women naturally have a larger hood and even when fully aroused the clitoris doesn't peep out.

Positions for his oral pleasure

Again, being comfortable is important while she's giving oral sex to him. Classic positions include her lying between his legs, or to the sides of them, or she can also do 'across the bridge' where she lies pretty much at right angles to him. Here are a few other Academy suggestions:

Worshipping at the altar – She kneels between his legs while he's standing. He might want to stand with his back to a wall so he can relax back into it. She reaches up and hold his hips to help steady her while she gives him oral sex. She can also easily caress and stroke his bottom if he likes that stimulation. If she's up for it this might lead to a classic Pearl Necklace where he comes over her neck or face. Obviously it should be her prerogative to say no if she doesn't like the idea.

Kneeling pose – She lies flat on her back with him kneeling over her chest. She can cradle his testicles with her hands as he tilts his penis into her mouth. He needs to control his thrusting because this can be a slightly awkward position. She can help control his thrusting by gripping his hips.

Picking the plums – This begins with him kneeling on the bed; he rests on the back of his legs, leaving his penis and testicles free to play with. She can lie on her stomach, head towards his crotch, and arch up to reach his penis and testicles. Alternatively she can lie on her back with her head between his thighs. For the man who likes his testicles sucked this is the perfect position – while sucking them she can masturbate him with her hands.

Night of 100 snakes – Try this technique to super-pleasure him. Hold his shaft firmly with one hand but not to the point it causes him discomfort. Keeping that hand still, shower his glans with tons of little flicks of your tongue. These shouldn't be hard pokes but gentle fluttering flicks. He'll love the very different sensations – from the firm grip to the little flutters.

Other oral pleasures

Many people like the sensation of gentle biting and nibbling but it takes some skill to do this during oral sex without hurting your partner. Both of you need to be careful of the tender skin of your partner's genitals.

As with every little technique, some people love it and some hate it. Those who don't like a little nibbling might find it a turn-off because they worry they're going to get hurt. A human bite is full of germs, so if you both like the idea of playful biting just don't break the skin.

When there's a risk of accidentally hurting your partner through biting and nibbling, it's probably best not do it when you've been drinking – you're more likely to have an accident. Safe areas to nibble include the inner thighs, lower abdomen or buttocks instead of biting the actual genitals.

If you're exploring their erogenous zones with your mouth, other areas for little bites include behind the knees, around the ankles and the back of the neck. Vary the sensations you give your partner by beginning with oral sex and then perhaps move to start nibbling and pulling on the skin around their belly button.

> *Academy tip:* **If you're celebrating a special occasion use a sip of the bubbly to add tingling sensations to your oral sex. Take a sip and then slip his penis – or her clitoris – in your mouth so they get bubbly sensations tingling all over the sensitive spots.**

Sex-tra oral considerations

Undoubtedly many couples have loads of fun putting chocolates and spooning creamy things into her vagina that get eaten out. But a word of warning here: exercise extreme caution when using something as a sex toy that wasn't made to be a sex toy.

Most people are smart enough to make an educated guess about what might make for some good sticky fun and what might get you into trouble when it comes to makeshift sex toys. Obviously never insert anything into any orifice that's made of glass or anything that might break.

Another consideration is that you might decide to use something for sex play that's actually covered in germs – very unhygienic. Even something as innocuous as a bar of soap can potentially irritate the delicate pH balance of the vagina or rectum, causing lots of discomfort. My rule of thumb is that apart from a little innocent bit of chocolate-play (or other sexy sauces) you should stick to purpose-built pleasure-toys. Definitely add in using a vibrator for extra oral pleasure but not a makeshift one. Have fun but play carefully.

Deep throating

Far too many porn films give men the idea that 'deep throating' is the ultimate erotic pleasure as well as being an easy technique to do. It's not! Mainly because most women find their gag reflex takes over and they gag when they take his penis even near their throat.

Another important aspect of this is the deeply uncomfortable 'choking' sensation many women feel when trying to deep throat. That said, with a little sex-perimentation it can work and it's worth trying if she's up for it. She shouldn't feel the pressure to do so because he's been watching porn films.

The key thing is her being in a position where her throat is in line with her mouth. For instance, use some pillows for her head to gently fall over, the back of her head arching back over them a little bit. This alignment means she might be able to take him in more deeply even if it's not deep throating.

A massive Academy warning: Women should **never ever** practise deep throating with bananas – this is a terrible idea and if the banana breaks it could actually choke you.

Be aware of hair

Many women won't like his facial hair tickling or scratching their very sensitive genitals when he goes down. So if he has facial hair he needs to realise how unpleasant it might make the oral sex experience. Your facial hair might feel soft and silky to you but it could feel like sandpaper to her rubbing against her delicate clitoris or vagina. Check out how she feels about your facial hair – you can experiment by rubbing your chin on her inner thigh to see how she feels about it.

Shaven-havens

Sticking with the theme of hair, again porn films have given many men the idea that women are happy to have all their pubic hair removed – the classic Brazilian. If she's happy to do this it can actually benefit her enjoyment of oral sex – it gives him complete access to her most delicate zones. Many women report having heightened sensitivity after waxing or shaving – they get amazing orgasms. Food for thought for women who've been avoiding even experimenting with this.

Many women prefer him to have less pubic hair so that when they go down on him they also have easier access to his penis and testicles. Let's face it, if he has masses of pubic hair to get through it can be tricky.

Again this is a personal choice and preference – another thing for you to have a fun and light-hearted chat about. There are many popular waxes now available including the Playboy – a full waxing except for a little triangle left just on the pubic mound. The straightforward Brazilian is everything off, but you can ask the beautician doing the waxing for shapes like a heart or butterfly on the pubic mound.

Men can go for waxing – have it all off with the famous back, sack and crack – or they can shave some or all of their pubic hair off.

For an extra treat you can try 'vajazzling' which has become popular – where the beautician adds glitter and sparkly 'gems' to the pubic mound. Men can have this done too.

Academy tip: Simply run your fingers through your lover's pubic hair before you start giving them oral sex to get rid of any stray hairs. Avoids that unpleasant experience of getting them stuck in your teeth or throat!

When trying to create a hot and pleasurable experience with any sex technique, always consider things like lighting. During oral sex subtle lighting might really help a shyer partner to relax. But if your partner's sexually confident, turn the lights up a bit so you can get turned on looking at their most intimate places while you kiss and lick them.

Men report being quite surprised by how much the female labia 'blush' a deeper red as they become engorged with blood when she's excited. They also note that the clitoris expands and rises up from under the clitoral hood when she's turned on. And as they continue giving her oral pleasure until she climaxes they might notice how the clitoris retracts again at this point.

This can be your secret guide to the fact that she's not faking it if you notice these changes. Obviously women realise that his penis will grow and become erect with engorgement. So it's no surprise there when she starts kissing a flaccid penis and it grows bigger and bigger in her mouth and hands!

I hope all Academy students have paid attention in this Lecture Series. You should now be equipped to give and receive super hot oral sex.

Lecture Series 6 Sex-amination

Circle the answer that you think is correct. Count up your number of A, B and C answers and then check the answer key below.

1/ *Does oral sex involve penetrative sex?*
   A/ No, but it can lead to it
   B/ Not really
   C/ Yes, it does

2/ *Is 69 an oral sex position or a penetrative sex position?*
   A/ It can be either

B/ I'm not sure

C/ It's an oral sex position

3/ Is it true that oral sex is a great way to make women climax?

A/ Yes, definitely

B/ It might be

C/ No, they need full sex

4/ Is it a good idea to touch and stroke your partner while giving them oral sex?

A/ Yes, definitely

B/ It might be OK

C/ No, it's a bad idea to mix things up

5/ Should you ever do something like shave your partner's pubic hair after a night of clubbing?

A/ Not if you've been drinking

B/ I'm not sure

C/ Yes, because you'll be less inhibited

6/ When giving oral sex will a man notice any changes in a woman?

A/ Yes, definitely, her genitals swell and moisten

B/ Yes, definitely, she'll become moist

C/ Yes, definitely, she'll be making moans and groans

7/ Can a man's facial hair affect the oral sex he gives?

A/ Yes, definitely

B/ It might

C/ No, I don't see how it can

8/ What is a common worry most women have about deep throating?

A/ *That they might gag*

B/ *That they might swallow*

C/ *That they won't do it as well as porn stars*

9/ *Are safer sex practices important in oral sex?*

A/ *Yes, they're very important*

B/ *I need to check that out*

C/ *No, it's not penetrative sex*

10/ *Is Reach the Peach an oral sex technique done to women or to men?*

A/ *It's done to women*

B/ *It's done to both*

C/ *It's done to men*

Number of As: _____

Number of Bs: _____

Number of Cs: _____

❂ Mainly As: Astoundingly hot

You're going to make your partner very happy when it comes to oral sex. You paid attention in the lessons and let's hope you can put that learning to good use.

❂ Mainly Bs: Best pay more attention in lectures

Definitely ask for loads of feedback from your partner seeing as you haven't done very well in this sex-am. It might be a good idea to go back over some of the lessons in this Lecture Series.

❂ Mainly Cs: Could hardly do worse

You've failed and need to go back and re-study this very important Lecture Series. Oral sex is something that'll make your sex life so much hotter and spicier. And definitely get instructions from your partner as to what he or she wants when it comes to oral – the only chance you have of mastering this is to listen and learn. A 'C' answer to question 9 is a particular no-no!

Lecture Series 7

Higher Learning: Sex Techniques for Graduate Level

Academy students should now be well prepared for this Lecture Series on advancing your sexual technique. This Lecture Series includes putting your sexual fantasies to good use and introduces more advanced and hotter techniques to try.

Academy rule no. 24: **Students should pause and think before they say 'no' to a request from their partner to try something new. You might miss out on something that's super sexy.**

Lesson 1: An introduction to sexual fantasies

As the Professor of Pleasure I'm quite used to people looking at me as if I'm suggesting they're part of the 'dirty mac' brigade when I ask about their sexual fantasies. Unfortunately people jump to the conclusion that they must have a dirty mind if they have sexual fantasies. Nothing could be further from the truth – you're not a pervert or dirty-minded because you have an active fantasy life.

Only a small number of people fantasise about worrying and dangerous things – and that's for another book about serious sexual problems rather than for the Academy. If your fantasies do stray into dark, illegal or dangerous territory – and particularly if you think you might act on them – I seriously urge you to seek help from a psychosexual counsellor.

Having fantasies that stray into dangerous territory is a million miles away from having a fantasy life that strays into risqué territory like fantasising about having rampant sex with a work colleague who happens to be married.

Such fantasies about things you wouldn't normally do but are technically legal (there is no law against sex with a married person) are absolutely fine. Most people would confess to having fantasies about married colleagues, their boss, their best friend's partner, etc. The human brain is incredibly creative so it's hardly surprising it creates such a variety of fantasies and is often labelled our biggest 'sex organ'.

Academy alert: you might also run into trouble with fantasies that become an obsession. For instance, if you fantasise about having a relationship with your favourite celebrity – and you can't get this out of your head – it could overwhelm your life. Such fantasy obsessions can prevent you from having a real relationship with a real person.

Thankfully the vast majority of people have harmless fantasies that stay just that – as fantasies. It's crucial you don't feel ashamed of harmless fantasies; they can be positively helpful in spicing up your sex life.

Variety is the spice of life

Let's face it, if you had the same dinner every night – steak and chips – you'd get bored very quickly. Your palate would quite rightly long for fresh flavours. It's the same when it comes to our thoughts about sex. Variety does spice things up. And if you have an active sexual fantasy life it'll help keep you interested in sex, particularly in a long-term relationship.

It's positively healthy to imagine various sex scenarios and it can give you lots of ideas for trying new things with a partner. All of my suggestions in this Lecture Series are obviously aimed at responsible adults who do not wish to harm themselves or anyone else. Having mentioned the word 'harm', the exceptions to this are people who practise S&M – who are we to judge such practices between consenting adults?

> _Academy fact:_ **Sexologist boffins go where no one else dares tread – they've researched how many of us have hot sexual fantasies. A whopping 94 per cent of men and 90 per cent of women confess to them … the rest are fibbing if they say they don't have sexual fantasies.**

Fantasies are so easily stimulated

When it should usually be a source of pleasure, some people feel worried about how easily fantasies pop into their heads. It only takes one glance of a woman's cleavage for a man to fantasise about a so-called 'tit-wank' – where he climaxes between her breasts. A woman might catch sight of a rippling bicep when a male friend picks up something heavy and find herself fantasising about having him there and then. A flirty salesgirl can easily arouse a fantasy in a man out shopping. A ruggedly handsome police officer stimulates a fantasy about men in uniforms in some women. And so it goes on.

Here's an important thought – people always talk about how 'men are very visual creatures' (I do myself). We all know how they immediately start fantasising when they catch sight of a bit of thigh under a short skirt or see a sexy actress in a film. But recent research has discovered that women are also equally visual creatures. It found that women experience

vaginal arousal when shown a variety of sexy images – including images of gay men! So don't underestimate the power of
the world around us to stimulate fantasies.

Put them to good use – spin that brief fantasy into a sexy
fantasy tale to describe in delicious detail to your partner, or
use that fantasy to privately stimulate you when you're a bit
tired but your partner wants to have sex.

Here's a checklist every good student should memorise
A healthy fantasy life has many benefits:

- ❂ It helps you escape sexual boredom.
- ❂ You get double the pleasure – you share your secret fantasies and your partner shares theirs.
- ❂ When your partner's away, fantasy-chat makes phone sex
  more fun.
- ❂ When you can't be with your lover (or you're single) and
  want to enjoy some self-pleasure, your active fantasy life
  makes this easy to do.
- ❂ In your private fantasies you can be with anyone – even
  people you'll never meet like your favourite celebrity.
- ❂ Sharing fantasies gives you and your partner fresh ideas to
  try – like some role-play.
- ❂ There are countless possibilities to be fantasising about.
- ❂ It's free!
- ❂ Your fantasies + their fantasies = endless fun in bed!

That's the huge benefit of having an active fantasy life – you
don't need money, you don't need props, you don't even need
someone else. Allow your mind to roam free and create a
wealth of erotic images.

Considering all these benefits I hope all students will affirm to themselves that it's positively good to have a fantasy life. You can always keep it private if you don't feel like sharing it.

Lesson 2: Sharing your sexual fantasies

At the risk of repeating myself, I'll remind you to mind your bedroom manners when sharing a fantasy. It's only good, decent manners to consider your partner's feelings when letting them into your secret fantasy life. You'd be surprised how many people confide in me how upset they were by the way a partner introduced a fantasy scenario.

If you want it to be an erotic experience you must think about the etiquette. The following are some bedroom basics that will make your fantasies sound sexy, not threatening.

Academy rule no. 25: Students shouldn't upset a partner by describing fantasies of sex with their favourite celebrity or a hot fantasy about your neighbour that excludes them. No, no, a thousand times no – it's very bad bedroom manners. Your partner should feature prominently in your fantasies – at least the ones you share with them.

Other erotic etiquette includes:

◐ Timing is crucial – if your partner's just confessed undying love for you that's not the best time to mention your kinky bondage fantasy. But in the middle of fun foreplay? Definitely ask if they have 'naughty thoughts' about secret desires. Using words like 'naughty thoughts' is gentler than diving in and asking about red-hot fantasies.

◐ When you feel it's the right moment to share some fantasy-chat sound your partner out. Cuddle and caress them and then whisper something sensual like, 'You're so gorgeous that I often fantasise I'm a photographer and you're a model that comes to my studio. You're not supposed to pose naked for the shoot but I slowly coax you into undressing.' This makes your fantasy arousing to them.

◐ Use what you're already doing to kick-start fantasy-chat. If you're gently rubbing massage oil onto them, describe lying on a tropical beach and that they're a sexy stranger who comes over to flirt. They begin rubbing suntan oil into your body and you two end up slipping off for amazing sex. Hopefully such chat will get your partner in the mood for sharing their fantasies.

◐ Remember: variety is the spice of life. Don't always describe the same scenario, no matter how erotic you find it this can get boring. The whole point of fantasy-sharing is roaming into fresh territory.

◐ Ask in confident tones (to give them confidence) if they'd like to share a fantasy with you.

◐ Use your knowledge of your partner's personality to decide whether they'd prefer you to describe your fantasy first or whether they'd like to tell you theirs first.

◐ When describing your fantasy always put your lover in the middle of the action, unless logically they wouldn't feature in it, for instance, if you fantasise about a lap-dancing club. But even in that scenario you could include them as a client standing in the lap-dancing club watching you. It's plain common sense that you wouldn't describe your fantasy about having a threesome with two colleagues from work, excluding your partner!

◐ Think about content you can share – you might fantasise about men in uniforms, but if your partner happens to be a policeman he might find it a turn-off because that's what his work is all about.

◐ The proverbial 'they' always say honesty is the best policy but use this principle with tact when it comes to sharing fantasies. Complete honesty might be hurtful to a partner – for instance, if you fantasise about big-breasted women but you're with a woman who has small breasts, she is not going to like it.

◐ Fantasies change – so never be surprised if your partner describes a fantasy about exhibitionism one week and the next time you discuss fantasies they talk about being dominated by someone else.

◐ Even if your partner wants you to share your fantasies first, don't forget to ask about theirs. This is particularly important if one of you is more sexually confident or dominant in the relationship – it's easy to dominate the fantasy-chat.

◐ With a new partner turn fantasy-chat into a game where you have to guess their fantasy. This can reveal all sorts of juicy stuff to chat about.

◐ Always bear in mind that what one person fantasises about might be a nightmare to another person. Tact and common sense are key. If you fantasise about golden showers – one of you weeing on the other – this may sound frightful to your partner. Best keep it to yourself until you're really sure you won't put them right off.

◐ Some fantasies should probably never be turned into reality – for instance, fantasy chat about having a threesome might be a super turn-on, but for many couples the reality would be an unhappy experience riddled with jealousy and insecurity. Think carefully before acting out any fantasies.

◐ You might be with a partner who would never admit to fantasising – because of sexual inhibitions it's simply a no-go zone. With the best will in the world and with a lot of tact you still might get resistance from them. If you love and respect them you might have to accept this. If you're very respectful you might try occasionally mentioning something like 'I fantasise about seeing you in a micro miniskirt and high-heeled stilettos'. With such encouragement they might open up to chatting about harmless and gentle fantasies.

Hot Academy homework

When feeling confident enough to start sharing a fantasy, definitely describe one that boosts your partner's sexual confidence. Today's Academy homework is to dream one up ahead of time, so that when you're next in bed together you can whisper, 'You're so gorgeous. I fantasise I'm a customer where you work and start to chat you up. You flirt back and suggest meeting up at night. Things get so hot between us that we tumble into bed barely knowing each other's names.' This type of fantasy makes your partner feel fab – and that's the perfect starting point.

Academy game suggestion: A great game is taking turns deciding the next twist in a fantasy scenario. For instance, you start by describing how you get lost and go into a bar to ask directions. No prize for guessing there's a really sexy stranger (who looks like your partner – remember your manners!) sitting at the bar who starts chatting you up. Now your partner says what happens next, and so on. Take turns until you both get so excited you have to have full sex.

What secret fantasies run through your mind?

There have been various surveys conducted into what we fantasise about. Although the detail of a particular fantasy scenario varies between people, a number of common themes emerge. Themes like risk, power, control, surprise, danger, stranger sex, exhibitionism and forbidden fruit run through so many fantasies. **A strong reminder:** just because someone fantasises about having sex with a stranger or being taken against their will, for example, doesn't mean they want this to happen! There are many themes that both men and women fantasise about equally.

Here is a selection of themes that you personally might fantasise about or have been told by a partner:

Female fantasy themes

- **Lesbian/bisexual fantasies** – Same-sex fantasy scenarios are very common and usually don't imply lesbian or bisexual leanings. They're more about curiosity and often revolve around how different it would feel to sleep with a woman, experiencing the differences in the female body and touch compared to a man's.

- **Sex with a stranger** – Trying the idea of no-strings sex is super appealing because it's so off limits. Encounters with strangers are a complete no-go area for many women so the element of extreme naughtiness is a powerful turn-on.

- **Having carefree, uninhibited sex** – As many women feel quite sexually inhibited, a common fantasy theme is about letting go of their inhibitions and throwing themselves into sex with abandonment. These fantasies are about feeling carefree and not worrying about how they look.

- **Group sex** – It's not only adventurous people that fantasise about group sex: this is a common scenario among women who wouldn't dream of doing it. Again there are elements of abandoning caution, plus revelling in numerous sexual encounters.

◐ Sex with a repair or delivery man, your doctor or anyone providing *services* to you – Earthy and naughty, such fantasies revolve around common notions that men who work with their hands are also good with their hands. There's also an element of the 'damsel in distress' who calls for a plumber only to find that he's completely gorgeous and up for raunchy sex on the kitchen floor.

◐ Forbidden sex with a friend's partner, a sister's boyfriend, etc. – We're always so well behaved, so fantasy themes around forbidden fruit and behaving badly really turn us on.

◐ Exhibitionism – Another fantasy theme that allows many women to lose their sexual inhibitions. It's quite a release to flaunt yourself in your fantasy playing the role of lap dancer or a woman who's decided to dance in a nightclub uninhibitedly, with men gathering around to watch.

◐ Exotic sex, being swept off to a foreign country against your will and being kept as a captive sex slave – As with a number of the more daring, dark and risqué fantasies, women obviously don't want to be taken as a sex slave but such a theme frees them from sexual inhibitions. This is because such themes are about being taken against her will – it's not her choice. I repeat, a woman might fantasise about this but that doesn't mean she wants it to happen!

◐ Forced to strip – Being forced to show off their body is another theme freeing a woman from all responsibility for such behaviour.

◐ Being secretly watched/spied upon – A fantasy in which a woman can feel she's so sexy someone wants to spy on her. This isn't necessarily about some creepy guy watching but more likely a handsome hunk who finds her sexy and desirable.

- **Domination and bondage, discipline and sadomaso-chism** – Fantasising about what many people still see as taboo, such as domination, etc., is a safe way of pushing the boundaries. The powerful erotic tension in films such as _The Piano_ or _The Secretary_ are good examples of how the handing-over of power can become the stuff of fantasies.

- **Sex with a celebrity** – This is complete escapism for many women who enjoy fantasising about having sex with their favourite celebrity. Part of this theme might be that the celebrity finds her incredibly attractive and irresistible.

- **Lady of the manor and the stable lad** – This is a variation on dominant and submissive themes: who's in control? The lady or the stable lad? These themes allow so much variety, including having rampant sex with a 'bit of rough'. Such fantasies fuel the secret desires of many women to be ravished by rough hands (similar to the tradesman/work-man fantasy above).

- **Directing sexual activity with a novice or from a position of authority** – Risky territory can be covered in these sorts of fantasies. For example, she might fantasise she's a school-teacher – or a 'Mrs Robinson' who seduces an 18-year-old virgin. It allows a woman to venture into taboo territory.

- **The 'casting couch'** – Fantasies offering sexual favours in exchange for getting job perks are incredibly common. It's surprising how many women mix work scenarios with hot sex experiences.

- **Being taken forcibly or being forced by a lover to do a new and forbidden sexual practice** – Strictly taboo themes like being forced into sexual acts 'against their will' allows women to play out different roles. Another reminder: this doesn't mean in any circumstances that a woman wants to be taken forcibly.

◐ **Starring in a porn film** – It's common fantasy ground to wonder what it would be like to be a porn star that men lust over. The elements of such fantasies include wanting to be desired by everyone who watches the film, as well as being very practised and experienced at sex. The raunchiness of this fantasy also allows women an escape from feeling that sex is often too predictable and 'clean'.

◐ **High-risk sex where there's a chance of discovery** – Taking a risk is a popular theme with many women since many don't take risks in their sex lives. So scenarios like joining the 'mile-high club', having sex in the office stationery cupboard or in the toilet in a nightclub explore the thrill of sex where you never know if someone's going to discover you. But actually getting caught in the fantasy adds a whole other twist to her pleasure.

Male fantasy themes

◐ **Sex with forbidden people like librarians, nuns and schoolteachers** – Men take such fantasies to the limit including fantasising about sex with 'untouchable' women like nuns. Women are less likely to have lustful fantasies about such forbidden people as priests – though, as above, they do have forbidden fantasies.

◐ **Ravishing an unlikely lover** – Similar in nature to having sex with forbidden people, it can be surprising that men fantasise about unlikely sexual partners, e.g., the mouse-like librarian. But this is all part of feeling sexually irresistible even to women who wouldn't normally want sex.

◐ **Sex with prostitutes** – The male mind is ever curious about what it would be like to pay for sex. Fantasies often revolve around paying for really 'dirty' sex that they wouldn't ask a partner for. Sometimes there's an element of power because you have the money to pay for it.

◐ **Lazy sex** – Don't men just love fantasising about lying back and having everything done to them! This may reflect how they actually behave with a partner if they are quite lazy, or the fact that some men feel very pressured to satisfy a woman – these fantasies let them off the hook.

◐ **Voyeuristic fantasies** – Voyeuristic fantasies are extremely common. They include themes like spying on a neighbour as she gets undressed and gets into the shower, or watching another couple make love. This may explain why so-called 'dogging' is such a popular activity with men (dogging is where people seek out other like-minded people to have sex in front of, or with, usually parked up in a secluded setting).

◐ **Being seduced by someone forbidden in your personal life** – If only women realised how often men fantasise about having sex with a girlfriend's mother, their wife's best friend, etc. This theme is a continuation of the forbidden fruit theme. 'Playing away' very close to home is a massive no-no, but like women, men relish the idea of doing something dirty on their own doorsteps.

◐ **Watching lesbian sex** – The majority of straight men admit to fantasising about two women making love. There are many reasons why they find this fantasy a turn-on. Men say they enjoy the gentleness of two women making love; they also think it'll reveal all sorts of secrets about women and their sexual preferences. But such fantasies almost always end with the man being asked to 'finish off' the women.

◐ **Being a successful businessman** – The thrill of abusing their power as a successful businessman is the stuff of many fantasies. They fantasise about taking their gorgeous PA on the conference room table or having it off at the Christmas party with a couple of the office girls.

◐ Being irresistible to a sexy nurse – This fantasy appeals to a man's desire to be irresistible as well as to be nurtured by a caring but sexy nurse. Hot sex with a raunchy nurse with the curtains drawn in the hospital bedroom or cubicle is a common fantasy.

◐ Watching his partner having sex with another man – Of all the voyeuristic fantasy themes this is one of the most personal and oh-so-raunchy. Many men confide that they would secretly be excited to see their partner having sex with someone else. Often the fantasy finishes with him taking over and being better than the other man, or it might end in three-way sex. Some men are excited about having 'sloppy seconds' with their partner.

◐ Bondage, domination and sadomasochism – So many men satisfy their curiosity for BDSM through fantasy. Some interchange between having the dominant or submissive role and others fantasise most about one particular role. If they're being dominated it's often in a very aggressive way that they get turned on by. If they're doing the dominating often it gets really dirty and raunchy.

◐ Gay sex encounter – Although straight men don't like to admit it, many have gay sex fantasies. It's usually more about curiosity and trying a new experience than having gay tendencies, although for some men this might actually be the case.

◐ Being 'feminised' – Women are often surprised when they hear their partner fantasises about being feminised (wearing makeup and lingerie and women's clothes). Usually this is about wanting to give up their predict-able dominant social role and replace it with a more

submissive role. By far the majority of men who fantasise about this don't want a sex change or to become
cross-dressers!

○ **Having really dirty/raunchy sex with a woman who's
rough or 'unwashed'** – Such fantasies appeal to the baser,
earthier side of male sexual desire. The sex in these fantasies is usually raunchy, quick and rampant and they don't
want to be troubled by the 'niceties' of watching out for a
woman's hair and makeup during sex.

○ **Having sex with a pregnant woman** – The ripe breasts
and lush stomach of a pregnant woman arouse many men.
These fantasies are common but often kept secret because
men feel guilty about lusting after pregnant women.

○ **Group and three-way sex** – These fantasies are often
about comparing themselves to other men and fantasising
that their performance is better. They're also about having
multiple sexual partners to 'play' with – to let go and be
completely uninhibited and sex-periment in a way they
never have.

○ **Being the sexiest super-stud on the planet** – This is
another fantasy theme about proving themselves. This
fantasy puts him with an adoring sex partner who can't
get enough of him. This fantasy is all about boosting
his ego.

○ **Seducing a younger woman** – By fantasising about
having a younger lover the pressure is off his lovemaking
skills; after all, he can teach her a thing or two. Often these
fantasies involve a little prayer worship on her part – in
his eyes she views him as a sex god ... we can let him have
his fantasy!

○ **Seducing a stranger on a train, plane, etc.** – A sexy
(or furtive) look signals he's irresistible to a beautiful

stranger. An ego-boost type of fantasy – men like the idea
of having risky sex with a stranger when on the move. Very
James Bond!

◐ **Seducing a gorgeous film star or celebrity** – Men also
spend a lot of time fantasising about their favourite film
and pop stars. It's also an ego-massage type of fantasy – the
ultimate boost where a gorgeous, famous woman selects
them to satisfy her needs.

◐ **Being a police/prison officer that toys with a beautiful
suspect/prisoner** – There's lots of sexual control in such
fantasies. He gets to do what he wants to his prisoner or
suspect – and, of course, she is super hot.

◐ **Anal sex** – Because so many women are turned off by the
idea of anal sex this makes thoughts of doing the deed even
more irresistible. Practically anything that's taboo makes
great fantasy material – and having her enjoy it in his
fantasy makes it all the more explosive.

◐ **Directing or starring in a porn film** – Take any variation
of porn-film fantasies and pretty much most men will get
turned on by them. From being the director who gets to tell
porn stars what to do to starring in the film themselves – it's
a turn-on. Also men get aroused by the completely sexual-
ised environment of a porn film set which offers countless
opportunities for playing out fantasies on film.

A brief English lesson

Brush up your English by putting your imagination to work –
write a text or e-mail to your partner outlining details of one of
your fantasies. It's fantastic practise writing it and when you
get their very positive feedback you'll have the confidence to
discuss it during foreplay. Once you've learned to talk dirty in
an e-mail or text it's often easier to talk dirty during sex.

Lesson 3: From fantasy to role-play

Students mustn't assume that if they open up about their fantasies they have to act them out in role-play. That's simply not the case and some partners would feel quite vulnerable trying to role-play their fantasy. They might be happy discussing fantasies in detail as they caress each other – or even whispering the details of their fantasy while having sex – but nothing more.

But for those of you interested in taking things further into role-play, you'll find many benefits:

- ◐ Role-playing can be very liberating for a couple, giving lots of options for trying new things.
- ◐ It can build their sexual confidence because they lose their inhibitions when pretending to be a fantasy figure – like a sexy doctor or nurse.
- ◐ Your communication improves by acting out a role-play.
- ◐ It might provide a whole new way of relating to each other sexually.
- ◐ You discover new things about each other as there aren't any rules!

Rules of role-play

Of course, having said there aren't any rules, as with most sexperimentation you need to be thoughtful and tactful. So here are some etiquette basics:

- ◐ It's not a good idea to plunge into a role-play without some thought. Always have some sexy fun chatting through fantasies – then you can pick one you both find exciting. You learned above how to chat about fantasies in a tactful way.

◐ It's great to experiment with role-play, but there's no point investing in costumes just in case you find neither of you like doing it. You could spend a small fortune on doctors and nurses outfits (that medical theme is always popping up!) only to find you laugh all the way through the role-play and can't return the clothes.

◐ Think about the local laws – for instance, you might be chilled out and relaxed on holiday or your hotel has a beautiful beach. But don't do a role-play on the beach at night (like one about a hotel security guard who seduces the rich tourist) unless you're very sure you won't get caught – you don't want to end up in trouble.

◐ Don't imply that your partner isn't sexy enough in their own personality. It's easy to forget when you're asking her to pretend to be a sexy stewardess that she might feel you don't already think she's sexy. Always qualify requests by saying how hot your partner is and 'how much fun it would be' for them to pretend to be X, Y or Z.

◐ Never try to insert items into any bodily orifices that aren't meant to go there! You might be role-playing the room service guy who brings the champagne to a hotel guest. He finds her undressed and they get carried away and drink champagne. Then he tries to stick the end of the champagne bottle up her vagina for extra hot fun – a big no-no and no fun at all if the bottle breaks.

◐ If you both love role-playing, beware how much you end up spending on costumes and accessories. These things can be pricey. Try to improvise with the clothes you have.

◐ As with any other sexual practice, beware role-playing doesn't become an obsession that takes over your sex life. Believe me, it happens, and often one partner isn't happy about it.

Academy motto: **One of the best qualities a lover can have is thoughtfulness.**

Lights, camera, role-play action

Once you've decided on a fantasy you both think would be fun to role-play, check out what you've already got that might become an accessory to help act it out. A silky dressing-gown sash can serve as a pretend 'rope' that the bank robber uses to tie up the pretty bank clerk with. Or his dressing-gown might work as a king's 'robe' when he orders the serving maid to do his royal bidding.

If you decide to get more adventurous there are loads of role-play outfits available from internet sites – and these sites can spare your blushes.

Academy recommendations to get the action started

You both might want to get adventurous but don't know where to start. Nothing to be insecure about – with the best will in the world, if you've never role-played it's hard to know what sexy scenarios might translate best into acting out. The following are some of the easiest recommendations that don't need any particular costumes to make them work well. They are my long-standing favourites to recommend because I've had so much feedback from couples who have had good experiences with them:

Strangers in the night – Probably one of the most popular role-plays of all is 'strangers in the night'. It costs nothing more than a couple of drinks, isn't too threatening, can boost your sex life and doesn't require any special outfits. Agree in advance what bar or nightspot you're going to meet at. Preferably somewhere neither of you has been before so the experience is completely fresh. The plan is that you pretend you don't know each other and that you're both looking for a night of lust.

Arrive separately and let the role-play begin. One of you will start chatting up the other, pretending you're strangers (both of you should use false names to add to the role-play). Have fun putting on a different personality – maybe one that's more outgoing and very flirty.

Turn up the flirt-factor and imagine you're both after a raunchy night. At some point in the evening one of you can suggest taking the 'party' home. To make it even hotter, pretend one (or both) of you is married and desperate not to be found out. Keep up the banter and cover stories for as long as you want. You might find this gives you the confidence to try a new position or technique. Some couples make pretending to meet as strangers a regular event a few times a year.

Naughty neighbour – Another simple, cost-free and usually successful role-play where one of you pretends to be the next-door neighbour that needs to borrow something or has just moved into the neighbourhood and needs to ask them questions about the area. Obviously it doesn't stop there and the flirting moves into hot sex on your sitting-room floor!

This can be a brilliant role-play with no costumes or props required, just the willingness to get into it and be a dirty flirt with your neighbour. Neighbourhood hospitality has never been so exciting.

Emergency rescue – Medical personnel keep cropping up as fantasies and they also make easy role-play material. The versatility of these role-plays is endless. Pretend you're making a visit to the A&E department. Or one of you can play the medical researcher who needs to explore the sexual response of a willing patient. You might get super raunchy with one of you playing the lecherous doctor who's going to take advantage of their patient.

Although fun costumes like a naughty nurse's outfit add to the role-play, they aren't necessary. It's easy to start such a role-play if you're chatting about the fantasy and he slips into the doctor's role asking the patient to undress. And there you are in the middle of a role-play!

Damsel in distress – You may be the strongest, most assertive woman in the boardroom but playing the role of helpless female for bedroom fun can have great payoffs. There are so many potential role-plays. Why not pretend your car has broken down – after knocking on a stranger's (your partner's) door for help you end up having fast and frenzied sex.

Or a fire has broken out and he's the fireman that arrives to save you. Once clear of the danger, you look into each other's eyes and feel immediate lust for each other after a life-threatening event. Or you pretend you've tripped and fallen and he comes to help you up. As he does so he 'accidentally' slips his hand across your breasts or bottom. The touch is electrifying and you start flirting with each other. None of these scenarios need any particular props – just your willingness to get into the role.

Randy national park attendant – She's got lost on a ramble around the national park and asks him for help. What you don't realise is he's a smooth-talking and randy park attendant. He wants to lure you to his lodge (your bedroom will do!) and get you between the sheets. You end up having wanton and abandoned sex like you've never had before.

The raunchy repairman – The raunchiness in your role-plays continues with him pretending to be a repair man. All he needs is a pair of old jeans and a T-shirt to get him into character. Again, she's the damsel in distress and he's the one who's going to fix the broken pipe, etc. But because he looks so hot she immediately gets horny. Let the chat-up lines come thick and fast as you end up discovering just how powerful his tool is!

The boss/manager – An easy role-play – even if you don't have a desk at home, the kitchen table will do. Two great starting points for this role-play include one of you being called in for disciplinary action or to get a job promotion. If it's disciplinary action, the one pretending to be the manager can be very dominating. The other, as a good employee, does their bidding.

If the employee is receiving praise, the manager can lavish them with compliments which soon extend to sexy suggestions. She can make sure her skirt hikes up as she props herself on his desk. He can start stroking between her legs as he tells her what a great job she's doing and how appreciated she is in the company.

Academy note: These examples are only examples and students are expected to come up with their own role-play scenarios. Do try and use simple props from around your home to add a touch of reality to your role-plays.

Lesson 4: Developing further sex-skills and thrills

Developing further sex-skills is crucial to on-going relationship satisfaction, as well as to single men and women who end up in bed with someone new and would like lots of ideas for pleasuring them. Many let their inhibitions get in the way and forget that sex should be fun – whether in a relationship or as a single person.

Academy rule no. 26: Yes, have fun in bed, but there's a big difference between laughing with a sex partner and laughing at them. You should have enough trust so that if you do something that backfires you're not going to get laughed at.

One thing a couple can learn from people who are single and simply enjoying a fling or one-night stand is that when single you're much more likely to go with the moment and get completely into the pleasure of the encounter. Obviously this isn't always true as plenty of people experience terrible one-night stands, but for others it's sometimes the best sex they've ever had because they're prepared to experiment with someone they may not see again. In some ways this is quite sad because a long-term relationship should be worth the investment to keep things a little bit exciting – or at least on occasion trying something new.

Another very dangerous issue for long-term relationships is slipping into routines, including sexual routines that become completely boring. Yes, as mentioned previously, there's nothing wrong as a couple with having 'comfortable' sex where you know what you're going to get, but always make sure you're not taking things for granted.

The following lesson includes lots of little pleasurable, sometimes exciting things to try – you can think of it as a pleasure chest of tips and techniques. Treat it like a 'pick 'n' mix' that you occasionally dip into.

Academy considerations

- This isn't a definitive list of little sexy treats and thrills to try. Allow it to help you generate fresh ideas.
- It's crucial to make each other feel loved and respected, especially when advancing your techniques. The more trust

you have the more fun you can have trying things, because you won't feel vulnerable.

◐ An open-minded approach that's positive and confident will encourage this feeling of trust between you.

◐ Definitely take a refresher course from Lecture Series 5 on communicating in a tactful way when you want to hot things up.

◐ 'Date nights' are definitely to be recommended – feel free to treat these nights as a time to try new things.

◐ Keep the balance in your sexual relationship by trying to take turns to make suggestions. Often the more confident partner will be the one suggesting new things. A quieter partner needs a nudge in the right direction – they might be quiet but they may have a lot of racy thoughts!

Academy tip: **Before using any touching techniques, always warm your hands by rubbing them together or running them under the hot tap so your partner's skin doesn't get a chilly shock.**

Academy rule no. 27: **Don't be daunted by any of the following suggestions. Some are super hot and some are just good clean (or dirty) fun. If you're feeling daunted reassure yourself you're worthy of trying new things.**

Here are a series of sexy suggestions to give you hours of pleasure (many work well in role-plays):

Sexy 'show and tell'
OK, most Academy students will feel a bit daunted or squeamish about the idea of mutual masturbation – admitting to masturbation is embarrassing enough but actually showing a partner what you do might seem mortifying. But 99 per cent

of people would love to know how their partner touches him or herself. They can learn so much – and that knowledge can be put to good use.

Why not get started by whispering during foreplay that you'd like to show your partner how you touch yourself. As you'll both already be turned on, hopefully you'll have more confidence. Relax in their arms, lie back and gently start stroking your nipples, your pubic mound or your genitals.

Or without even mentioning it start doing this during foreplay. They'll soon catch on to the fact that you're stroking yourself. Touch yourself lightly and sensually. Tell them it'll turn you on if they watch. After a bit, ask them to touch you in the same way. This is where some fantasy-chat can help as you move into the role of 'sexy professor' – instruct them to do exactly as you do.

Dim the lights a bit (nicer for foreplay anyway) and it'll give you confidence to start touching yourself. Then slide your hand over theirs and start building up more vigorous stimulation. As you both grow in confidence you can enjoy mutual masturbation – when you both touch yourselves at the same time. Some of those blessed with super confidence can turn this into a floor show – showing off how they tease and please themselves.

The red velvet technique

The next step is for her to move her body against his – the slang for it is a bit of 'dry humping'. I prefer 'red velvet technique' as her labia are pink/red inside and feel velvety rubbing against him. Again, this can be highly instructive (a great excuse for getting a bit raunchy with it!) as he gets to feel the way she likes to rock her genitals against his body – learning the pressure, the speed and the friction she prefers.

Academy rule no. 28: Rock that body into theirs – don't leave any area untouched and under-stimulated during foreplay!

Silky scarf and panty play

This is a fantastic little trick for women who find it hard to let go or reach climax. It gives a lovely teasing sensation and the more teasing she receives the more likely she'll get fully aroused. Best to use a silky scarf that you don't care about as it'll end up covered with her natural juices. Alternatively use a pair of her silky panties.

Slowly and sensuously he can remove her silky panties and, taking them in his hand, lightly run their silkiness around and around her pubic mound. Next he can slip the silkiness down over her labia, around her perineum and back up again. Keep asking how many times she wants this raunchy cycle repeated. A perfect way to get her ready for full penetration.

The same technique can be done with a silky scarf. For another version of this technique, he can help her on to her side facing him and slip the silky scarf between her legs. Next he reaches one hand around behind her to grab one end of the scarf as the other hand grabs the end in front of her. He moves his hands – each holding one end of the scarf – up and down, back and forth, gliding across her labia. A very hot technique!

His royal 'studliness'

It's guaranteed he masturbates even when he's got a partner. In fact often men in satisfying sexual relationships masturbate more – that's because they're thinking about her and the great time they had in bed that morning, the night before, at the weekend, etc., and get excited.

Even if it takes coaxing he should show her how he strokes himself – either during foreplay (as above) or when sharing a shower together. Once he knows what pleasure he gives her he'll be like a proper stud wanting to show off his growing erection. And when he comes to ejaculating, with the right encouragement he'll turn it into a proper show. No mess or fuss if done in the shower together. She'll probably want him to get going a second time around – for full sex – after seeing the show.

Honey pie
During foreplay she can take mutual masturbation further by lying back and spreading her legs. She can fondle herself in full view with her fingers moving in and out of her wet vagina. He can encourage her to take her finger and lick it, tasting her juices. Next she can swirl her finger inside of herself and gently stroke his lips with her moist fingertips – it'll be as sweet as honey to him.

> **Academy sex suggestion:** After she fingers herself and wipes her moistness on her lips, she can kiss him full on the mouth so they both taste her love juices.

Honey lips
Lie back and enjoy this sweet and sexy oral sex technique. Keep a pot of honey by the bedside so it's ready to go. After some foreplay coax him on to his back – then she can straddle him so that he has access to kiss and lick her labia and vagina. Here comes the honey pot – she can dip a finger in and sexily spread a little bit on to her labia. The honey gets warmed up by the warmth of her skin so it slips over his lips and tongue as he gives her oral pleasure. She can sit there straddling him for as long as they want – occasionally dipping into the honey pot while he licks at her very own 'honey pot'.

Ripe as a peach

Fresh fruit has never been put to such great use! He can use this hot little trick when giving her oral pleasure. Having split a ripe peach in half he gently squeezes some of the juice over her labia. With his fingertips he can gently stroke her wet labia – spreading the droplets of juice around and around making her super turned on. Next he can go down for a taste – licking and kissing her before squeezing a little more juice on to her labia. Definitely use your favourite fruit – as long as you can get juice out of it. Anything ripe and juicy like melon, mango or papaya will do.

Subtle but winning ways

Tons of touching techniques have been covered in earlier Lecture Series but here's an advanced one for a man with skilled fingertips. He gives her G-spot stimulation in a very subtle way by applying gentle circular pressure with his fingers about four to five inches below her belly button – just above her pubic bone. This stimulates her G-spot area because it's located inside her, underneath this area of the lower abdomen. A little lower-abdomen massage can go a long way to making her feel super horny. Tease her – don't slip your fingers down into her vagina until she's really turned on.

The sexy snake

This is another sophisticated fingering technique he can try to stimulate the inside of her vagina. It can be used during foreplay or after mutual masturbation when you start touching each other again. This technique will probably get her turned on quickly. After some general caressing of her outer labia and vagina he puts his index and middle fingers together and, making sure they're well lubricated, he slowly slips them up inside of her.

Once inside he should rest his fingers for a moment before gently starting to wiggle them around inside her as a snake wiggles when it slithers. The great thing about this technique is that his fingers touch all of the inside walls of her vagina. The wiggling action alternates pressure on the different sides of her vagina. The sexy 'snake' gives a sensation that's like a vibrator on slow speed. If he doesn't like the idea of using a vibrator (a fair number of men don't) on her then this technique gives her the sensations of one.

Whole palm pleasure

While using your favourite lubricant, smear a generous portion on the palm of your hand so you can slip and slide over large erogenous zones. Why not have her lie back and open her legs. Then he can use the whole palm of his hand to massage from her pubic mound right down under to her bottom. She'll love big, gentle, sensual sweeping motions with his lubed-up palm.

As she gets excited he can slow the sweeping movements down to smaller strokes circling her clitoris, sweeping up and down her labia, and back around her clitoris. For a little bit of 'domination play' he can use his free hand to hold her thighs open. Combine this with some fantasy-chat where he is the 'mean, nasty boss' who's expecting her to 'spread her legs' for him.

She can give whole palm pleasure to him, too, and also combine it with some sex-chat about being in control of him and his pleasure. She can sit astride him facing his feet. With his legs open she has easy access to use big, pleasurable sweeping motions with her whole palm up and down his testicles and perineum, down under his bottom. And then her hands can come back up over the whole of his shaft. As she's sitting away from him, he can caress, pinch and even slap her bottom for extra pleasure.

Double hander delight

Give them double the pleasure by putting both your hands to good use – this is a different version of the double hander previously described.

For her pleasure: he can ask her to lie on her back as he crouches over her. He places his hands on her breasts and gently circles each breast with his hands. He can then shift his gentle and sensual circling action to the tips of her now erect nipples.

As she gets aroused he can then move one hand back and forth, circling and stroking her nipples, and move his other hand down to her pubic mound to lightly stroke back and forth. This double stimulation will feel heavenly to her.

For his pleasure: she can try the double hander technique when crouching over him or kneeling to the side of his hips. She can gently and sensually stimulate his penis by stroking his shaft up and down with one hand. Then she can slip her other hand gently between his thighs and rub her fingertips back and forth over his perineum. This will be heaven to him.

A touch of fetishism

The next Lecture Series will include fetishes, S&M, B&D, etc., but use this tip for a touch of fetishism. You can slip on a pair of gloves (obviously clean ones, but a pair you don't mind messing up) with a texture your partner has a preference for – soft and velvety, smooth and silky, firm and leathery. Then apply lots of lubrication and tease and please their erogenous zones, stroking them with this new sensation.

Academy sex trick: Most people are left- or right-handed and their preference shows through in their sex-play. Partners will often end up on the same side of a bed – the side they're most comfortable with – making it easier to use their preferred hand for foreplay. But one little trick is to swap sides or swap hands to touch and stroke your partner.

If your partner closes their eyes they can pretend it's someone else touching them – not that they'd want to! Enjoy the different feelings you can create with this simple trick. It's not a good idea to swap hands right before your partner climaxes if you've brought them to that point with the other hand. This could stop them in their tracks – incredibly frustrating.

Lesson 5: Strip tease 'n' please

Couples who have let go and at least dabbled in stripping or 'amateur lap dancing' for each other usually have a great time. It takes confidence to start but can be super exciting. It's perfect to try when you've had a lovely evening, you're lying back and enjoying foreplay and one of you suggests a bit of stripping. And this goes both ways – one survey found that many women loved it when their partner did a fun strip for them.

Here are some stripping tips to get you started (most of these apply to both of you – guys, you can get your clothes off too!):

- Boost your confidence by practising some moves in private. No one has to know that you're secretly bumping and grinding in front of your bedroom mirror.
- Get a feel for the moves you feel the most confident with. You might feel comfortable holding on to the door as if it was a dancing pole and moving your hips back and forth in front of it rather than doing a full bump and grind in the middle of the bedroom floor.

- ❍ Imagine the moves that a real stripper/lap dancer does to help create your repertoire. Even go so far as to role-play being a lap dancer or male stripper – it can help you let go of your inhibitions.

- ❍ Try out different kinds of music to see what you feel confident moving to. You might prefer a big classic rock tune or some moody, smooth R&B.

- ❍ You might feel happiest only stripping off to your bra and panties. Your partner needs to respect that. It'll definitely boost your confidence if you're wearing a new knicker set which you think sets off your curves.

- ❍ If you're going to fully strip off make sure you start in a dress or outfit that isn't hard to pull off with loads of fiddly buttons! It's not very sexy if you get stuck trying to undo something in the middle of your moves.

- ❍ Like any good Academy student you should always be prepared – so once you're happy with some music leave the CD in the player ready to put on when you're in the mood.

- ❍ Have candles in place or subtle lighting when you decide to go for it.

- ❍ Sometimes it can boost your confidence to strip as a gift for a birthday or anniversary present.

- ❍ Definitely try stroking and touching yourself the way a lap dancer does to boost your self-belief that you're going to look hot. Remind yourself that your partner is going to love it!

- ❍ Don't get anxious about trying things that are too complicated. Keep it simple – they're going to be focusing on what an amazing surprise this is.

- ❍ You could ask your partner to stay on the bed or sit in a chair to watch.

- ❍ Go to town – try different things like tying their hands to the chair so they can't reach out and touch you. Again, use role-play techniques: for instance, you can pretend to be a very strict stripper who doesn't allow touching of any sort. Then wiggle right in front of him and push his head between your breasts. Or he can swivel his hips, shaking his penis right in front of her eyes.

◐ You could try some proper 'research' for your strip routines and check out a stripping or lap-dancing club. An increasing number of couples are going to these clubs and find they have pretty rampant sex afterwards.

◐ If you're still not sure about practising on your own, there are stripping/lap-dancing classes offered in many gyms and health clubs.

◐ Try using silky materials in your teasing strip-play – when you're confident moving in front of your partner, take a silky dressing-gown sash, slip it between your legs and move it back and forth the way strippers do. Or run it across your thighs and breasts, teasing your nipples so they become erect.

Academy history lesson: Victorian pleasure

Now that you've done some stripping-off, you might want to try something else a bit revealing. We all know the Victorians had complicated attitudes towards sex, seeing it as dirty, so they were particularly keen to wash their genitals before and after sex. And because they didn't trust a new partner to be 'clean' they'd often wash their genitals for them. This can actually be turned into something hot, even raunchy. So why not have your partner lie back and turn this Victorian habit into a sexy little treat where you gently wash (and stroke and tease) them with a warm cloth. Gently and sensually washing between their legs and allowing the warm water to trickle down can be quite ritualistic – and arousing.

Victorian pleasure II

We can learn more from the Victorians' sex lives – they loved the eroticism of spying on a stripper, for instance. They'd carve peepholes into Oriental screens to watch sex acts, stripping or even an unsuspecting lover. Such voyeurism plays into a 'peeping Tom' fantasy and you can have fun doing a bit of role-play. Do this by allowing your partner a glimpse of flesh during foreplay. Or titillate them by walking around in something skimpy but forbid them touching you. Oops, you've dropped something and need to bend over (in a short skirt) to pick it up. Such little role-plays can lead to lots of dirty fun.

Feminising fun

As mentioned before, many men won't admit it but they often enjoy a bit of gender-bending. If she's up for it – and understands this doesn't make him 'gay' – it can be naughty fun. The more confident the man, the more likely he is to try a little feminisation. Putting on some mascara, a bit of lippy and maybe slipping into some of her silky knickers has nothing to do with being gay or straight. It's far more to do with role-play around how submissive and dominant or how traditionally masculine he is – and maybe he'd like to break out of that mould in the privacy of your sex life.

Don't fear – feminising doesn't mean he's turning into a transvestite. It's simply him using a little makeup and/or slipping into something feminine. He might prefer to feminise himself or for her to apply the makeup, etc. But once feminised definitely get into some fantasy-chat and even role-play. It's your secret pleasure!

Going commando

Thinking of having sexy secrets between you brings me

to a little trick which can add spice to your sex life. How about agreeing to go commando (no underpants/knickers) when you're out. Only you two know that neither of you are wearing your smalls at a restaurant or a friend's dinner party.

Have fun with the 'easy access' that going commando provides and touch each other under the restaurant table. It can also lead to a quickie once you're on your way home – no knickers to fiddle with, just up with her skirt and down with his trousers and away you go.

You can even be a little bit outrageous and surprise your partner by announcing you're going commando when you're out doing something like clothes shopping. They'll ask you for more detail, like if you're feeling horny being out with no knickers on. Have a quick grope somewhere private with promises for more back home.

Sex slave massage

With the submissive/dominant theme arising from feminisation, definitely don't miss out on the chance for sexy chat. One of you can role-play being the sex slave while the other is the master or mistress. The master/mistress orders the sex slave to give them an amazing massage. They need to prepare the 'boudoir' – candles lit, music on, massage oil and sex toys to hand. The room is warm, or they've just taken some big soft towels out of the dryer to wrap the master/mistress in.

Then they give you a top-to-toe experience of pleasure – they touch you exactly as you order them to. From delicate and sensual touches to using your favourite vibrator on you – anything goes. Play fair; next time they get to be pleasured by you.

Lesson 6: Porn and related pleasures

A little porn pleasure

Watching porn as a couple is not to everyone's taste, and no one should ever be pressured into watching it, but there is plenty of porn made with couples in mind – not just adolescent males. The good thing about 'porn-lite' is it can give you various ideas for fantasies. If it's never come up but you're keen to watch it with your partner, approach it tactfully:

- Don't just bring home a porn DVD – always ask first if your partner's interested in watching some.
- Definitely start with something 'vanilla' – not hard-core porn! The high-street adult shops tend to have couple-friendly porn.
- Once watching the DVD, don't go on about how sexy the porn stars are – this is completely tactless and hurtful.
- Only start shagging while watching the DVD if your partner wants to. They might feel quite vulnerable having sex while watching porn – and might want all your attention for themselves.
- If it's a good experience – and you both enjoy it – then keep it for occasional sex sessions. It's surprising how many people can end up relying on porn for sexual satisfaction. And that's not a healthy way to conduct your sex life.
- Use the experience to kick-start a porn star/director fantasy.

Filming for your private pleasure

If you've been inspired to make your own video, bear in mind you might be a couple now but after a breakup such things can find their way onto the internet. Unless you have a very stable relationship, destroy your films after watching them.

Amateur videos can end up a big turn-off and very disappointing, so think about a few basics like the lighting and the way you position yourself. She won't be happy if the camera has made her bottom look much bigger and he won't be happy if it's made his erection look smaller. Experiment with different angles and then go for it. Hopefully you'll end up with many moments of viewing pleasure.

Go wild

Thinking about filming makes me think of old-fashioned bodice-rippers. Experiment with letting go – or quite literally letting rip – with some older clothing that still looks good but you don't mind damaging. Have fun playing the captive woman as a handsome but dominating pirate rips your top off. Or let the dominating office manager snag your tights, pulling them off too quickly because he can't wait to get into your knickers. Some people have a fetish (salirophilia) for messing up clothing and makeup before having sex.

Academy rule no. 29: As with all fetishes, never force yours on a partner – unless they want to try it.

Getting intimate on the internet

Many have discovered the joy of cybersex, particularly in long-distance relationships. Sharing a webcam experience with your distant partner means lots of sexy fun. Roaming the net for sex sites, etc., is something else entirely. It definitely serves a need for many single and horny people, but there are two main dangers – the first being that you stop relating to people face to face and only have net sex. Secondly, if you're in a relationship and start flirting with another man or woman through cybersex – thinking it's harmless fun – it can actually destroy your relationship.

Don't underestimate the addictive power of sex websites to draw you in and take over your life. Definitely beware of sites that charge – sometimes incredibly high prices. It's a slippery slope to getting in debt. If you know you have an addictive nature I'd recommend completely avoiding cybersex.

Apart from that, using a webcam with a partner can be extremely exciting. You can put to good use your lessons on talking dirty and stripping.

If you're going on a site because you're single and looking for excitement, remember never to give away any personal information. Remember that if you post a film of yourself – maybe pleasuring yourself – it could be seen by millions of people, not just one person on a particular site.

Don't arrange a face-to-face 'date' with anyone you've had cybersex with – they might seem sexy and fun at the other end of the webcam but you don't know what they're really like. If you're determined to meet someone then use very strict dating precautions like taking a friend along with you and meeting in a public place during the daytime.

Phone sex

In Lecture Series 5 you learned how to 'finesse' dirty talk – all students were given top tips for talking dirty without turning someone off. Use these tips for raunchy fun during phone sex. You might find you let go of inhibitions because you can't see your partner's face and reactions. Many people confide in me that they think they're sexier talking on the phone than when they talk to their partner in bed.

It's a great way to start sharing fantasy-chat – it's late in the evening, you're in your separate homes, you're relaxed in bed and you find yourself saying dirty things you haven't before. Go for it but use the same tips previously outlined.

Lesson 7: More titillation, thrills and teasing

Breast sex-play

One thing she'll undoubtedly describe over the phone to him is how much she loves touching her breasts. And one thing she might describe is giving him a 'tit-job' the next time they're together. This will blow most men's minds as many men really do like the idea of thrusting gently between her breasts.

When together, try doing it when she is relaxed. She lies back and he can squeeze loads of luscious lubricant all over her breasts and abdomen. He can tease her and massage her breasts before getting in position for a bit of breast pleasure. She can sit on the edge the bed and he then stands in front of her. She can squeeze her breasts together and he nudges the end of his penis between them. It can help for her to knit her fingers underneath her breasts to support them.

He should be gentle and only go as firmly she can take. She needs to feel confident enough to tell him to 'go easy' if he starts losing a bit of control. As his sexual tension builds they can go for full sex, or if she doesn't object to a Pearl Necklace he could come on her.

This is a great scenario for using dirty talk – he can murmur how amazing her breasts feel and she can say how amazing his cock is. In advance agree where he's going to ejaculate – and have tissues handy for him to ejaculate in if she doesn't want a Pearl Necklace.

Let every part of you get in on the action

Academy students should now be aware that at any time

they might be combining a number of techniques. Having insisted you exercise your PC muscles in earlier lessons you should now have great PC muscle strength. Put them to good use and create a sizzling sensation with a long 'squeeze' technique. Having previously described pulsating these muscles, squeeze onto the shaft of his penis and hold for three or four of his deep thrusts. He'll feel your grip and it creates a powerful friction between you and his thrusting. It can lead to equally powerful orgasms for you both.

Brushed and buffed

Take your new-found creativity into your general mindset. When you're messing around, flirting, maybe getting into foreplay, be aware of what you might use to heighten pleasure. Say he's come up behind her in the kitchen and wraps his arm around her. As they start kissing – and maybe more, as kitchen counters and tables are rather popular for quickies – take what comes to hand, like a basting brush (obviously clean). Dip it in some olive oil and tease and swirl the oil across his chest or her breasts.

Take it further with something edible like chocolate sauce and paint numbers on your partner's body. You have to kiss and lick your way around these numbers in order.

Tempting teasing

Definitely take teasing to new heights – unless you want a quickie, get your partner as frustrated and excited as possible before you have full sex. This works especially well for women who aren't very orgasmic – the more they're teased in the way they like, the more likely they'll climax. Tempting and teasing are hugely underrated – we want things NOW but waiting can make them even better.

Academy teasing tips for her to try

- ❂ When you're both super-sexed-up after lots of foreplay, she can sit astride him and rub her well-lubricated labia up and down the length of his shaft. She can tease him as long as they both can take it ... careful: he might explode as he watches her breasts moving along with her pelvic moves.

- ❂ During any rear-entry position like the Spoons or Doggy she can gently take the shaft of his penis in her hand and start rubbing the tip of his penis up and down her labia and around her clitoral region. She can do this after he's done some thrusting or before he starts, or she can occasionally interrupt thrusting to use the tip of his penis in this super stimulating way.

- ❂ She can gently push him away after his first few thrusts during penetration and hold him a few inches away from her vagina. He can feel the heat coming off her body and she teases him more by allowing him to move closer and just touch the end of his penis to her labia before pushing him away again. Such explosive tactics can make you both pretty breathless.

- ❂ Partial penetration can be a big turn-on. If she keeps her panties on and he pulls them aside and slips into her it can be a big tease because he can't get all the way in.

- ❂ Or she can keep hold of his hips and prevent him thrusting any deeper than she wants. When neither can take it any more she can allow him to fully enter her.

He can try the following techniques:

- ❂ He takes control in any 'on top of her' position where he holds his erection and gently teases her clitoris with the tip of his penis. This can be done when straddling her, sitting astride her or kneeling between her legs. He can hold the shaft of his penis and simply rub it in slow, sensuous, circular motions or up and down her labia.

◗ He can take this a bit further and gently circle her clitoral region with the tip of his penis before moving on to stroke up and down her labia.

◗ Next he turns up the heat and nudges the end of his penis inside her – maybe giving her a few gentle thrusts before withdrawing again.

◗ This is a good technique to use when you share a steamy shower together – he can nudge the tip of his erect penis between her legs and around her clitoral region.

◗ Get creative and move in different ways with thrusts so he stimulates her labia and vagina.

◗ He can definitely turn the full thrusting into something more creative and exciting than repeatedly going in and out. To get her fully aroused and lubricated he can use gentle, slow, circular thrusting. This takes a lot of control and the more experience he has the easier he'll find it to control such super hot movements. If she thinks she may have a G-spot, the circular thrusts are fantastic for investigating whether she does!

◗ While teasing each other it's the perfect time to introduce some fantasy-chat. He can pretend to be the 'massage' expert who has to feel with his penis every bit of the inside of her vagina. He can talk about wanting to completely penetrate her and she can describe exactly how his 'pulsating, erect cock' feels.

Thrusting technique tip

To develop his thrusting control he can use this fun technique which will help him learn how to use gentle and sensual thrusts. Stroke and caress each other's bodies with some lovely massage oil. Have an ordinary balloon (yes, a balloon!) to hand, blown up to about three-quarters capacity. Slip this between your bodies and he'll need to move gently to try to keep it in place and avoid bursting it with his thrusting.

Period pleasure

Learning how to thrust gently can come in handy when she's having her period. Obviously some people wouldn't think of having sex during her time of the month but others are more open-minded and are happy to. She should definitely use some of the fantastic Beppy Action Tampons that look like large, soft marshmallows. They're inserted into her vagina and can't really be felt during sex.

Female ejaculation

Getting creative, trying different thrusting styles and teasing every bit of each other brings me to the final point of this lesson – that elusive female ejaculation. This is hotly debated by sex researchers. The way I view it as a sex writer is that sex-perimenting to find out whether you, as a woman, can ejaculate can be a positive thing. Obviously sex-periment without pressure and in the spirit of getting to know more about the way your body responds sexually.

No woman should feel pressure to experiment or feel bad if she doesn't 'ejaculate'. What some sex researchers believe is that female ejaculation is potentially due to a lot of stimulation of the front wall of the vagina (the G-spot and A-zone). This allows a build-up of fluids (not urine) that are released – or ejaculated – during an intense orgasmic experience. Some women report this stream of excess fluid as far more than the normal moisture/lubrication they get in their vagina when aroused. If this doesn't appeal to you or doesn't happen, DON'T worry about it!

Lecture Series 7 Sex-amination

Circle the answer that you think is correct. Count up your number of A, B and C answers and then check the answer key below.

1/ When sharing a secret fantasy, does timing have anything to do with it?

A/ Maybe, it depends on what fantasy you want to share

B/ Yes, timing is crucial

C/ No, I can't see how timing fits in

2/ Are women 'visual' like men when it comes to getting sexually excited by what they see?

A/ They might be

B/ Yes, definitely

C/ No way, men are so easily excited by seeing something sexy

3/ What is the 'sexy snake' technique?

A/ It's a sexy tonguing technique

B/ It's a sexy fingering technique

C/ It's a sexy position

4/ What is a good starting point for stripping for your partner?

A/ Definitely to watch some strippers

B/ Definitely to practise on your own and to choose easy-to-take-off clothes

C/ Definitely to just do it

5/ Are 'group sex' fantasies popular with both men and women?

A/ No, just with women

B/ Yes, they are

C/ No, just with men

6/ Is it a good idea for men to thrust inside their partner in a 'circular' motion?

A/ It might work

B/ Yes, this can have definite benefits for her

C/ No, this would feel just plain weird

7/ Should a couple ever watch each other touch themselves?

A/ Maybe, if they both agree

B/ Yes, definitely it's exciting and shows each other what feels good

C/ No, touching yourself should always be private

8/ Can a woman have sex during her period?

A/ It's possible

B/ Yes, especially if both partners are happy about doing so

C/ No, don't be disgusting

9/ Why would a woman ever fantasise about being a porn star?

A/ Because she'd like to see what it would be like to be bossed around by the director

B/ Because it would allow her to feel less inhibited and behave in a super raunchy way

C/ Because she likes watching porn

10/ What is 'whole palm pleasure' good for?

A/ It's a different way of touching

B/ It's good for stimulating larger erogenous zones

C/ It's good for holding hands

Number of As: _____

Number of Bs: _____

Number of Cs: _____

◐ Mainly As: Answers could be improved

If you pay more attention you could be a good Academy student – try harder in the next Lecture Series.

◐ Mainly Bs: Best in lectures

You've absorbed much of the content of this Lecture Series and are ready to move on to even more advanced graduate-level techniques.

◐ Mainly Cs: Caught out – you haven't studied enough

Oh dear, you've let yourself down terribly. I'm not sure whether you should move on to the diploma-level Lecture Series without further study!

Lecture Series 8

Ensuring Your Diploma in Sexual Achievement

This final Lecture Series will develop further your specialist knowledge. I hope the following lessons induce a spirit of sex-perimentation in Academy students and encourage you to occasionally push boundaries.

Lesson 1: Some sensual spiritual techniques

'Spiritual mixed with sex?' I hear many Academy students asking. Yes, the spiritual side of sex was embraced by the original Tantric practitioners, who have a lot to teach us. Unfortunately most people switch off the minute they think of Tantric sex. They wonder if Sting and wife Trudie were really 'at it' for hours at a time – and if so how boring that must've been.

Whatever Sting did or didn't get up to doesn't matter; for Academy purposes you're simply going to learn about a few techniques that'll add to the sensuality of your sex life. Certainly Tantric practitioners have a lot to offer when it comes to sensuality and engaging all your different senses during lovemaking.

It's worth taking a moment to try the following tips – they might help you gain more intimacy with your partner.

Academy motto: **Intimacy leads to trust – and trust leads to turning up the heat.**

Academy tip: **Your partner may be sceptical about whether there's anything to be gained from 'hippie-ish' Tantric sex. Simply assure them a few simple techniques might well lead to more powerful orgasms.**

Tantric breathing

Let's begin with the most basic technique – Tantric breathing. Take the opportunity when lying side by side, perhaps early in foreplay, to allow your bodies to touch lightly. Suggest that you both close your eyes and begin to breathe in sync with each other – feel the rhythm of your partner's chest rising and falling. Lying quietly, holding each other, you'll start to feel your ribcages moving together.

Now all you need to do is relax and breathe 'as one' for five, ten or more minutes. Just enjoy the sensation of being connected through your life breath. Many report they find this emotionally satisfying. They feel a deeper and emotionally intimate connection. And when you feel more intimate it improves your physical connection, too, by increasing subtle communication about your physical state to each other.

Tantric heartbeat

This takes Tantric breathing to the next level and can make you feel really connected by coordinating the beating of your hearts. One of you moves on top of the other and lies there gently. Both of you should be comfortable so that you can keep still and quiet. Your chests and abdomens will be touching and by lying there quietly you'll begin to sense the other's heartbeat.

This can develop sensations of closeness and emotional

bonding, as well as being quite soothing when you hear the murmur of your partner's heart. Even if you find your heart rates are very different it can still be very soothing.

The million-dollar spot

Tantric techniques also involve sensual touching and practitioners were among the first to emphasise the sexiness of a man's 'million-dollar spot'. This is located on his perineum – the site varies between being nearer to the base of his testicles or to his back passage, depending on the man. Think of this spot as lying above (on the outside) the location of his prostate.

Have fun locating it:

- ○ Turn down the lights, slip on to the bed together and tell him you want to find a super sexy spot on him.
- ○ Have some lubricant or massage oil handy – warm your hands before you touch him.
- ○ He should lie on his back with his thighs relaxed apart.
- ○ Remember the location of the million-dollar spot – on the perineum, the area of skin between the base of his testicles and his anal opening.
- ○ Most men don't get the chance to experience the pleasure of getting this spot stimulated, so he might be quite sensitive or even ticklish.
- ○ Because of this she needs to be aware of how he's responding to her touch.
- ○ She can either lie with her head resting on his pelvis – her hands free to roam between his legs – or in a more dominant position crouching in between his legs.
- ○ While he closes his eyes and relaxes, she gently rubs, strokes, teases and massages his perineum with well-lubricated fingers.

◗ She can be guided by his sex sounds as she touches him.

◗ When he feels she's found his most sensitive, erotic zone he
   should let her know.

◗ If he wants her to she can continue stimulating him here
   with a vibrator.

***Academy tip:* For added pleasure why not shave his pubic hair,
at least underneath his testicles, so she has easy access to lick
this area. She should try pulsating her tongue to stimulate the
million-dollar spot.**

Once they both know where his spot is located she should
definitely stimulate this area when she gives him oral sex
in future. Also depending on the sex positions they use she
might be able to reach this area to apply pressure just before
and during his orgasm. He needs to guide her on how much
pressure is necessary to intensify his climax.

The whole body orgasm

This might sound like a tall order – a whole body orgasm.
But it's worth giving this technique a shot as you can achieve
powerful orgasms. If you try it and feel it doesn't benefit your
climaxes then nothing's lost, but potentially you could have a
very hot time.

For starters you need to do the opposite of what you
normally do as sexual tension builds when you get nearer to
climax. So focus on producing the opposite response in yourself. Both of you need to know the following tips in advance:

As foreplay is heating up and you start getting excited that
full sex is on the agenda, first listen to each other's breathing
and begin to move together. The point of this is to synchro-
nise your general movements.

When your breathing feels like it's becoming in sync with each other, that's when you should start having full penetrative sex.

As penetration begins (and usually that's when your muscles begin to tense as climax seems on the horizon) you need to begin relaxing your muscles – this is the opposite of what you'd normally do. You might find it helpful to gently whisper and remind yourselves to relax your muscles. This can feel strange at first but it's worth trying.

Next it's time to become aware of your breathing again and do the opposite of what you normally do during full sex. You'd normally find that your breathing gets quicker and shallow as your excitement builds. But now you need to slow it down and avoid it becoming shallow.

As you're relaxing your muscles and slowing your breathing the final technique is to try and clear your mind of any thoughts. This includes fantasy thoughts – and it can be quite tricky stopping those. All you should be thinking about at this point is relaxation for your muscles, slow and steady breath control, and listening to your partner's responses.

If you manage all of these, you might find that when you reach climax it ripples powerfully throughout your whole body in a way your orgasm normally doesn't. If you find all of this too distracting, of course just enjoy sex the way you normally do.

Lesson 2: Anal pleasures

Most men and women will admit in confidence that they're at least curious about anal sex, even if it isn't top of their list of secret sexual desires. Having covered anal-play in previous Lecture Series, we'll now look at full anal sex.

Traditionally this has been seen as the 'forbidden fruit' of sex and for a long time it was actually forbidden even in our

Western, liberal-minded culture. But that's not always been the case and cultures like the ancient Sumerians had very open-minded attitudes towards anal sex.

What's the fascination with anal pleasure?

Despite being legal now it's still considered pretty hot stuff. Unfortunately porn films featuring anal sex scenes give the wrong view that it's easy to do, pain-free and always pleasurable. That's just not the case and people vary tremendously in whether they love it or hate it – and all points in between.

Those men that enjoy penetrating their partner anally say they get a different sensation to vaginal sex. Those women who enjoy receiving it also experience different sensations. And if they have the chance to whip on a strap-on and 'do' him it can be an exhilarating (and usually dominant) feeling.

Academy safer sex reminder: Even if you're engaging in only a little anal-play – and not full anal – you still need to be very aware of safer sex methods. Always use barrier methods such as those described previously. Throughout the rest of this Lecture Series there are further techniques that require safer sex methods unless you know each other's sexual history and are free of STIs.

In the beginning

If you have a partner who is shy/inhibited about trying anal sex definitely begin with the gentler anal pleasures described earlier. As always, no one should ever feel forced to try it. A person who's been coerced into trying something like anal sex can go off sex altogether because they feel such negative feelings around their sexual experiences. You don't want that to happen.

Academy dos and don'ts for successful anal sex

There are basic but necessary steps to take to have an enjoyable anal sex experience. The following steps are written as if she's going to be the 'receiver', i.e., he's going to penetrate her. However, they equally apply to him if she's going to stimulate him with her finger, a vibrator, a strap-on, or if he's going to have gay sex:

- ◗ Do I have to remind you that no one should ever be pressured into anything like anal sex if they don't want to?

- ◗ Do discuss in advance trying a little anal penetration. You'd be surprised how many people spring this suggestion on an unsuspecting partner in the middle of a sex session – this doesn't usually meet with a positive response.

- ◗ Do use a good-quality lubricant that's condom/latex-friendly. Unlike the vagina, the anal passage doesn't lubricate itself.

- ◗ Definitely re-apply lubricant for anal sex that goes on longer than a few minutes. The rule is that you can't apply too much or too often!

- ◗ Do select condoms that are labelled durable, etc., as anal sex by its very nature puts more pressure on a condom, therefore it's more likely to split.

- ◗ Do empty your rectum if you plan to have full penetrative sex. It can be emptied either naturally or with the help of a suppository purchased from the chemist.

- ◗ Do expel any trapped wind. Not only can it be embarrassing to pass wind in the middle of penetration but it can also be uncomfortable. This can be easily done by slipping into the bathroom for privacy. Getting down on all fours tip your pelvis upwards as trapped wind rises. This is probably the most effective way of expelling trapped wind if there is any.

◐ Do make sure her anal area and your hands are clean before you get started with initial anal-play. Even if you're simply going to stimulate her with your finger, it's easy to spread germs from this potentially germ-laden area. Equally you don't want to pass on any germs from your hands to her anal area.

◐ Do trim your nails (which will also be clean!) so they don't cause her any discomfort.

◐ Do generate a relaxed vibe between you. Being relaxed can make all the difference to anal penetration. Any tension means her sphincter won't relax. Considering that anal penetration is the exact opposite of what the sphincter and rectum were made for, this is absolutely critical.

◐ Do lavish her with plenty of foreplay – it'll help arouse and relax her.

◐ Don't go for full-on anal penetration straight off. It can be difficult and you should indulge in some anal-play beforehand.

◐ Do try initial stimulation first: put a condom or latex glove on your finger, cover it with lubricant and try fingering her anus. Begin by inserting one finger gently and leave it there without moving it. Allowing it to rest like this helps the outer anal sphincter to relax. Or you could indulge in a little anilingus or 'rimming'. Or try a little 'tickling' around the rim which can help them relax their sphincter if they like the sensation.

◐ Do keep checking how they're feeling – ask if they want you to pump up the action, move your finger a bit more, nudge it in a bit further, etc.

◐ Do go for a gentle position like classic Spoons when you first attempt penetration. Alternatively, if she's well supported with lots of pillows/cushions try Doggy style.

◐ If it's a success and you're physically fit, do try one of the other more technically difficult positions I've already outlined in earlier lessons – many give good anal access.

◐ Do suggest that she tries a bizarre-sounding, but useful tip as he starts penetration: to help temporarily relax her sphincter she should make an action as if she's passing wind; he can enter more easily at that point.

◐ Don't feel like it's a failure if penetration can't take place. It can take a number of attempts; or the person being penetrated might decide they don't want to try it any more.

◐ Do be aware of the fact that even if it's been a pleasurable experience, she might experience pain or discomfort for a couple of days afterwards.

Academy secret revelation: In confidence many straight men admit to being curious about anal penetration, but they're very concerned their female partner might think they're harbouring gay desires. With about 30 per cent of strap-ons sold to straight couples (the rest to lesbian couples) men are becoming increasingly honest about trying this out.

Academy anal sex suggestions

Here are a few carefully selected ideas for you to try:

Double delight – Lots of people report that they love the sensation of their orifices being completely 'filled up'. If you enjoy that sensation try the following:

For her pleasure: Try this in the Spoons position (quick reminder: both on your sides, him behind her, facing her back). She can choose her favourite vibrator for vaginal stimulation. Once she's totally aroused, enjoying the sensations of her vibrator inside of her, he can gently begin anal penetration. She stays in control of the vibrator action while he concentrates on his thrusting.

For his pleasure: Don't fret, he gets his share of 'double trouble'. Try this technique while in the Lovers' Embrace position (facing each other on your sides). Either he can have a butt plug inserted before he starts thrusting or she can reach around his hips and stimulate him with an anal vibrator.

Pro-jobs – He can thank the sex trade for this super hot technique involving both oral and anal pleasure. I've named it the 'pro-job' after meeting various sex workers in a professional capacity. When I've asked about the secrets of their trade, many have told me how a man will often pay for this extra pleasure when he comes to a sex worker for oral sex.

While she gives him a blow job she also anally penetrates him with her finger. To keep safe she should slip her finger into a latex glove or a condom to prevent transmission of germs between her finger and his anus.

She can build his excitement by starting very slowly with her fingertip gently easing into his anus. Then she gently feels for his prostate area – he should be giving her feedback when it's feeling good. Alternatively while sucking, licking and kissing his penis she can use an anal vibrator on him. Blow jobs will take on a whole new brilliant dimension for him.

He shouldn't forget to return such double pleasure for her when he next goes down on her. She might like some anal stimulation when he's giving her oral sex.

Make your mouth sparkle – For his added pleasure when she starts a pro-job (or a blow job) she can sip a mouthful of something sparkling (champagne, beer, cava, fizzy drink) and then wrap her lips around his penis to give him an extra tingling sensation. You can get the same sizzling sensation by putting a little toothpaste, mint or Alka-Seltzer in your mouth before sucking his penis. Of course when he goes down on her he can do the same thing to give her clitoris and labia this sparkling, tingling sensation.

> ***Academy caution:*** **Some of the tips in these lessons are not for the faint hearted. For instance, some men might think a pro-job is a step too far – they might feel too 'exposed' with her mouth around his cock and finger up his butt. So instead of actually doing some of these tips you might want to use them for racy fantasy-chat. Just because you don't actually want to do something doesn't mean you can't talk about it … in loads of hot detail.**

Butt plug lust – Once they've tried them, many men and women enjoy wearing butt plugs. As noted in Lecture Series 4, butt plugs come in different sizes to accommodate … well, different needs and desires. Buy a 'matching' pair of butt plugs (sometimes a bigger size for him) and wear them out and about as you go about your daily business. For some other butt-plug fun go out to dinner with friends or business associates secretly wearing matching plugs. You'll both know why you can barely sit still in your seats and the secret stimulation will get you ready for action later.

Bottoms up – If you want to discover if he enjoys having anal stimulation then turn a back massage into something more. Have him lie on his stomach while you smother him in luscious lubricant. Stroke his back up and down and add a vibrator for extra sensations. Then move on down to his bum cheeks and swirl around and around them with your lubed-up fingers and the vibrator.

Now take control, part his cheeks and pleasure him anally with the vibrator. Turn it into some fantasy-chat – you're a dominatrix and you're going to have your 'wicked' way with him. He may not want you to stop pleasuring his cheeks, perineum and rectum. Carry on the pleasure with him in missionary position and you reaching around with the vibrator to tease him anally.

The buttock bonk – Some things that he might desire may not sound exciting for her, like the 'tit-job' in the last Lecture Series – it might be some women's idea of hell and others' idea of super exciting. The same goes for the buttock bonk – women love it or hate it – but you might just make his dream come true if you get into the Doggy position and allow him to thrust gently between your bum cheeks. This still requires safer sex practices, but he might enjoy whipping off the condom just before he climaxes to ejaculate over her bum cheeks and lower back. As long as she doesn't find this offensive, why not try it for a bit of dirty fun?

Lesson 3: Daring, dirty and even rude tips, tricks and techniques

Before we get to a few fetishes, a bit of bondage (and more), here is a sprinkling of suggestions for Academy students to sex-periment with:

Wet and wonderful

Part of the pleasure of good sex is all the wet and wonderful sensations – from having loads of luscious lubricant all over you, to your own natural lubrication when aroused, to getting hot and steamy in the shower together. There's something people love about wet and slushy sex.

There are all kinds of wet fun you can have besides messing around in the shower. For starters, protect your bedding by laying out a towel on the bed. Squirt a long stream of your favourite massage oil or lubricant along the top of their pubic bone allowing it to drip down over their genitals and then you can gently start stroking and massaging it in. This can be hot, hot, hot!

The cascade

After drizzling lubricant down their breasts/chest, stomach and hips add a vibrator for extra fun. Gently trace the vibrator on low speed across their breasts and nipples, then swirl the lubed-up vibrator down their abdomen. This is the perfect way to tease them so they're gagging for sex. Make them wait as you apply more lubricant and continue with gliding motions up and down their erogenous zones.

Wet indulgence

To super-indulge your partner run a bath for them. Make sure the bathroom is warm and there's a dry towel ready, then touch and tease them as they relax in warm water. Everyone loves being spoilt and it's amazing how sensual it feels to orgasm in a warm bath while you do nothing but relax.

Faux water sports

So-called 'water sports' involve playing with urine. This is more popular than you might guess, despite the fact that there is a high risk of transmitting STIs through water sports. Some people simply like being urinated on or urinating on another person. One of the more extreme versions involves him urinating into a plastic hose that's inserted into her vagina. It sounds disgusting to most people, but each to their own for consenting adults.

So why not fake it? You can do a bit of dirty sex-perimentation with 'faux' water sports. Here's how to fake it: brew some weak herbal tea, like camomile, which looks fairly like wee once cooled. Get into fantasy-chat mode – you both might enjoy some super dirty chat with this one. Have your partner lie face down so that you can drip the cooled tea on their back (note I stress cooled – you don't want to burn them!). Or take things back into the bathroom: you can stand over them in the bath and as you pour the innocent tea over them you dirtily chat to them as if you're doing a water-sports fantasy.

Rub a dub dub

Mutual masturbation was discussed in the last Lecture Series, but here's a tip from female masturbation. Most women love a rubbing action between their legs, spreading the stimulation right across their pubic mound, labia and vagina. Many women confide that they use a soft cushion between their legs to pad out the feeling of their hand and to get this lovely rubbing sensation. To re-create this orgasmic sensation he can encourage her to 'dry hump' (as it's called) against his thigh. Rub some lovely lubricant across her so she can slip and slide to her heart's content.

She'll need lots of 'permission' from him to give her the confidence to rub herself like this. But if she has any problems reaching climax this is a great way to help her. She might have more confidence to do this under the covers – when they've been kissing and cuddling in bed – and she can quite naturally start rubbing herself against his thigh. He can say things like 'It'll turn me on to feel you rubbing yourself against me'.

Flashlight fantasy

Speaking of under the covers, here's a bedtime game to ensure a sexy romp. Academy students should get creative with things around the home, and in this case you'll need a torch – plus a raunchy sense of humour. Keep the torch at your bedside and when you're both in the mood for some fun play 'explorers' under the sheets. One of you has the torch and has to dive down under the sheets to get a torch-lit view of all their partner's intimate places. Get ready to do some very intimate touching and licking.

Turn it into a game where they have to plant a lingering kiss where the torchlight has landed. Of course both of you should take turns diving down between the sheets and exploring fresh territory.

Alfresco sex

Having had loads of indoor pleasure, it can be quite exciting to have some outdoor (alfresco) sex, as mentioned in the earlier location lessons. (Be careful not to get in trouble with decency laws.)

There's something about doing a sex act when you might get caught that makes it terribly exciting. Because we're so used to having sex 'under wraps' in the privacy of our bedroom (and even under a pile of duvets/sheets/blankets), it completely takes us out of our comfort zone to have sex outdoors. It stimulates every single one of our senses and adds an electrifying feeling that you're doing something risky. This taps into our primal side (that in ancient times man used to be ready for sex whenever it was available) that nowadays is subdued by the way we live. Just talking about adventurous sex can help a couple bond at a more intimate level.

Academy top tips:

◐ Always have something to throw over yourselves to cover up if someone comes past. For example, if you're on holiday and you decide to have sex on a reclining beach chair at your hotel on a star lit night, then bring along a big beach towel to throw over yourselves if need be. You can smile innocently if someone strolls past, pretending you're just cuddling up together under the towel.

◐ The other big no-no is thinking you can get your partner to have sex, say, out in a forest or field and not think about their comfort – naughty you! Always have a picnic blanket or at least a thick jacket to put under them for their comfort. Or take along a cushion to pad out any tender body part (e.g. their bum) that may have to press against something like a stone wall or tree trunk.

◐ Another trick is to pleasure each other with your hands or through oral sex when outdoors. One of you can keep watch for anyone approaching. It heightens your sense of risk.

◐ Perhaps simply start your foreplay when out and about – and save finishing each other off for when you get home. This can lead to exhilarating sex.

◐ Bring sun cream for any under-exposed body area that may see the light of day – like your bum!

◐ If one of you simply isn't sure about doing it outside, a good compromise is fantasising about what sort of alfresco sex you could get up to. Take turns suggesting the twists and turns in the fantasy.

Share her juices

When alfresco it's sometimes best if one of you goes down on the other so one can 'keep watch'. Take this oral pleasure a bit further and try this kinky tip: when he goes down on her and she's getting very wet he can suck some of her juices into his mouth. Then he moves up to kiss her on her mouth and shares droplets of her juices with her. Very intimate and very horny! He can go back down on her as much as he wants and then kiss her again.

Baby you can drive my car

You might decide you'd rather park up and have some steamy car sex – the best position for this is the Cowgirl, where she can ride you to her heart's content. Lower the passenger seat and lie back. She slips on top of him, facing him but still sitting over him – not lying flat against him. She may not be able to bounce up and down too much but you should get good thrusting action and penetration.

Vibe for two

Outdoors it might work best if you play with some vibrators. Get comfortable side by side but turned towards each other so you can reach each other's erogenous zones. Both of you are armed with vibrators to stroke and caress the other with. Tease each other to the point of no return by stroking back and forth across their pubic bone. Just enjoy the sensations of knowing you might get spotted at this beauty spot and then take turns bringing each other to climax.

Adrenalin buzz

Turn having risky sex into something special by showing up at your partner's office with little or nothing underneath your coat. You don't have to have full sex – you could pretend to talk seriously with them when all along you're describing how sexy you feel underneath that coat. Sneak off to a discreet corner and allow them to touch you under your coat. Maybe chat about an office-based fantasy while you're at it. You'll both be buzzing and ready for raunchy sex later that night at home.

Lesson 4: Three-way or group sex

Threesomes and group sex definitely seem to be becoming more common, with one survey revealing that 19 per cent of people are keen to have a go. As a way of spicing up your sex life it's certainly become more acceptable and couples are often happy to talk about their experiences.

Having interviewed many couples who've tried this, I'm not surprised to find that some of the relationships have been blown out of the water, usually through jealousy – one partner gets very jealous seeing the other partner have sex with someone else. These practices work best for couples who have strong confidence and trust in each other; most people should probably keep this in the realms of fantasy-chat.

If you have your heart set on trying this, definitely follow these Academy ground rules:

- ◐ For starters you both should find discussing three-ways and group sex a huge turn-on in fantasy-chat.
- ◐ Next, having agreed you both really like the idea, you need to consider first the possibilities of jealousies and insecurities. Discuss these potential feelings honestly.
- ◐ If you're both happy to go ahead you need to check out local swingers' groups or specialist sex contact magazines and websites.
- ◐ Tread very carefully about having sex with a third person that you both already know, e.g. a friend.
- ◐ It's important to agree specific rules. For instance, some couples may not want their partners to engage in oral sex. Discuss these things completely openly.

- It's crucial to keep open communication going between you – this helps prevent insecurities or jealousies developing.

- Agree whether or not you'll revisit the same swingers' group or have the same threesome, bearing in mind there's potential to form attachments if you have repeated sexual encounters with the same people. It's surprising how quickly new relationships form when in these highly sexed situations.

- You need to agree that if you go ahead and one of you doesn't enjoy the experience they won't be under any pressure to do it again.

- Definitely 'debrief' after these sexual encounters to make sure both of you are feeling OK about what's happened.

- Finally, you'll need to agree to set boundaries on any extra contact you have with any of your new sexual partners. For instance, will you be allowed to chat to them on the phone or will there be no further communication?

Dogging

Dogging has often been in the press for the last decade. As mentioned earlier, it's a type of group sex where drivers find out about secluded locations to park up and have sex with others watching or allow others to join in having sex. Remember, doggers have different preferences and even if you both want to try it you might have very different ideas about what turns you on.

There are many dogging websites that give local information about where these activities take place. Be aware that you still need to apply some of the basic rules above to dogging. Also be very aware that doggers have their own codes for signalling what activities they're happy to take part in. Something like switching on the internal light in your car might mean you're happy for others to watch you and your partner in action – but people aren't allowed to join in.

Lesson 5: Fetish fun

As the word fetish is bandied about on a daily basis, people know it's a casual way of defining practically anything someone is sexually aroused by. Men will say they have a 'fetish' for large breasts; women will say they have a 'fetish' for men in gym gear.

In reality, this casual use of the word fetish downgrades its original meaning. Its true meaning would be that a man who says he has a fetish for large breasts could only get aroused by women with big breasts, and the woman who claims to have a fetish for men in gym gear could only get excited around men wearing gym gear.

But that's simply not the case for most people making this claim – they can be turned on in all sorts of ways. For a true fetishist it's a different story. They need the object of their fetish to be present to get turned on. Or they need to have a good strong fantasy life that provides them with an image and powerful thoughts of their fetish.

There are a vast variety of fetishes and in fact practically anything can become a fetish. Many fetishes are completely harmless, like men turned on by women in short skirts or women turned on by men in football strips. But of course fetishes can be more bizarre, like salirophilia – the desire to make someone less attractive, to mess up their hair or clothing. And some fetishes can be downright shocking, like scat-play (coprophilia) – being aroused by faeces. Most of us quite understandably find such fetishes completely bewildering and wonder how on earth a person could find such things sexually arousing.

How a fetish begins

You may well end up being with a partner who has a fetish or you might have a fetish yourself. Particularly if your partner has a fetish, you might long to understand why they have it. For the purposes of television and radio programmes I've interviewed a variety of fetishists. Sometimes there's a very firm starting point that the person remembers, for instance, that the first time they had sex as a teenager it was standing in the rain in a wet field and their partner had wellington boots on. So good old wellington boots become their fetish and their sexual excitement is connected to this detail of that first experience.

So a sometimes complex process can be simplified and you can think of a fetish developing when sexual arousal occurs in the presence of an _unrelated_ stimulus. A so-called unrelated stimulus then becomes sexually charged itself – like the wellington boots.

Sometimes the development of a fetish is very complex and it's difficult for the person to work out where their desire came from. Fetishes can also develop later in life, not only through early sexual experiences.

Academy rule no. 30: Those with fetishes should not expect their partner is going to embrace them. Good communication between you can help work out a compromise or another solution to your different feelings towards a fetish. Obviously if you're worried about your fetish you should consult a healthcare professional/ sex therapist about your concerns.

B&D and S&M

Many fetishes involve bondage and domination (B&D) and/ or sadomasochism (S&M). Putting aside extreme fetishes for strong B&D and S&M, many couples enjoy a bit of fun with some of the 'vanilla' fetish items, like buying handcuffs or a spanking paddle.

Let me clarify the difference between B&D and S&M. Bondage and domination revolves around restraint, control, developing sexual tension, teasing and usually giving verbal commands to a lover in order to get them to 'submit' to your demands. Sadomasochism is more likely to involve actual pain as well as degradation. Having said that, different people will mix the boundaries on these – there's a lot of crossover between the two.

Sex Academy isn't going to cover any extreme B&D and S&M practices. Those are of a specialist nature – and if that's your thing you probably know where to get information and the gear to satisfy your desires as well as knowing where fetish and bondage clubs are. However, for the students wanting to spice up their sex lives there are lots of tips and techniques to follow.

Play safe
Even if you're not doing hardcore B&D and S&M, people can get carried away and end up in the accident and emergency room. Here are some important Academy tips to follow:

- Do communicate honestly about the sorts of things you have in mind. For example, explain you'd like to be handcuffed and have your partner role-play being your captor.
- If you're doing anything like tying up or handcuffing each other you must agree a code word! This is a neutral word that tells the other that no matter what you're doing you want to stop. Use a neutral word so that during the height of passion it can't be confused with wanting to carry on if for

example you're engaged in role-play. For instance, if you're playing a kidnapped victim who falls in love with your captor and you say something like 'Don't, please don't!' it could be taken either way – as part of your 'character' or that you actually want to stop. A neutral word can't be misunderstood.

- NEVER be pressured to try something you find frightening or that would turn you off.

- Don't EVER try anything dangerous like auto-asphyxiation where you restrict your own airways or restrict your partner's. The Academy message is don't restrict airways!

- Don't do any bondage sex-play when you've been drinking or taking recreational drugs. This sounds overly protective but alcohol and drugs alter your inhibitions and notions of what's safe and not safe. They can change your pain threshold too.

- If you're going to whip your partner, never do so near their face – you don't want to take their eye out!

- Also beware of whipping their genitals – a laceration can lead to serious damage.

- NEVER leave your partner on their own if you've restrained them. It's not a joke to try to scare them because accidents can happen.

- You've tied the knot, for example with a silky dressing-gown sash, so make sure you know how to untie it.

- If something feels uncomfortable when you first start – like a handcuff that's too tight – it'll only get worse. So ensure your partner's comfortable when their hands are tied behind their back, for instance.

- Never restrain any area for too long. You've already been warned about cock rings and the same should apply for other restraints.

- While getting dirty with each other, keep it clean. Always consider hygiene when someone's tied up and you're both aroused, for example. Don't get carried away using a vibrator in her rectum and then put it in her vagina.
- Being restrained in bondage-play definitely heightens sexual tension. The restrained person can only wriggle around while the dominant partner stimulates them.
- There are a wide range of restraints available from adult shops and internet sites, but before you invest in any, experiment with your partner using a soft dressing-gown sash or similar – perhaps a soft leather or soft material belt to strap their wrists together. Always make sure circulation isn't restricted.
- Try some of the ready-made 'bondage sheets' with velcro straps for the ankles and wrists. You can play safe with these by tying your partner to the bed for some teasing action.
- There are tons of little accessories that go with 'vanilla' B&D and S&M like nipple and genital clamps to add a little bit of pain/pleasure to your sex-play.

If you and your partner would like to try restraining each other here are suggestions to get you started:

- Tie/restrain your partner's hands together or separately. Alternatively, tie their hands to the bedhead/bedstead or with long sashes to the legs of a bed or chair. Allow some movement for the rest of their body so they can wriggle around as the 'detective' teases them, trying to get them to answer questions.
- You can try restraining/tying their elbows together. Pinning back her elbows pushes her breasts out if she's the one being dominated. However, this position can get uncomfortable so you'll need to tease her straight away.

◐ Moving on to the legs, you can bind your partner's knees. This can give an unnaturally tight squeeze for penetrative sex – definitely worth trying if you're into experimenting with different sensations.

◐ Ankles have been considered erotic since Victorian times, so try strapping their ankles together. Or tie their feet together or separately to the bedstead or legs of a chair – now they won't be able to escape from the 'dastardly' sex-play you want to do to them.

◐ Get seriously dominant and if they agree, expose your partner's genitals during bondage-play that literally puts their most intimate parts on display. You can ease them over the back of a comfy armchair and tie their legs apart with their ankles bound to the chair legs. This is not for the faint hearted but can lead to fantastic sexual tension when you tease them orally or with sex toys.

◐ If you find you both get into fetish play there are lots of specialist fetish manufacturers that can provide everything from fetish chairs to your own 'dungeon' in your spare room!

Some tempting techniques to try:

Get spiky

She can give him a mix of erotic pain and a back massage by blindfolding him and having him lie on the carpet on his stomach. Definitely pad your carpet with some soft, warm towels or blankets for his comfort. Test his pain/pleasure zone by first gently digging your stiletto heel into his back. If he likes it then very carefully walk on him with your stilettos – he'll let you know if it becomes too painful.

Dress for bondage bliss

There is a huge variety of bondage gear to try. Don't go over the top kitting yourself out completely in a latex body suit, for example. Instead choose one piece to create the right impression – think of your partner's preferences for things like leather, PVC or rubber. You might choose to wear thigh-high boots or stilettos paired with a rubber miniskirt. Add a see-through blouse and you're on your way. Definitely add to any dominatrix-style role-play by wearing the colours associated with domination like black and scarlet.

There's plenty of bondage-type gear for men too – he might want to try something like a genital bondage strap or a leather thong complete with studs.

Bound and gagged

Once you've got a few things to set the scene like ties, sashes, ropes, handcuffs and blindfolds, you'll probably find a lot of fantasy and role-play (a few suggestions sprinkled above – detective, pirate, etc.) come quite easily. Take advantage of this new lack of inhibitions to get creative, especially with roles you play out.

Academy fact: Couples that indulge in bondage-play say it allows them a lot of freedom to experiment with taking the dominant role, the submissive role and crossing between the two.

Play and display

She'll need confidence for this, but it can lead to raunchy fantasy role-play. Tie her ankles apart with a soft sash so that her legs are completely opened up. She can lie in bed with one ankle tied to one side of the bed and the other ankle tied to the other. Or she might prefer sitting in a chair and you tie her ankles wide open.

Turn up the heat by enacting a raunchy role-play with her at his mercy – he teases her with lots of touching, feathering and caressing. He might even take a well-lubricated vibrator and run it up and down her labia. If she's up for more restraint she can have her wrists handcuffed with the soft, fur-lined ones. He can bring her to the point of climax and then finally release her for what will probably be fast and furious sex.

Academy motto: Always play fair – he should have a turn having his ankles tied apart and being teased with a vibrator or any way she wants to pleasure him.

Sensory deprivation

While we're thinking about tying up your partner – or you being tied – also consider sex play with blindfolds. You immediately heighten the sensitivity of your skin once blindfolded.

Blindfolds can be used in many ways. They can help restore sensuality for a couple who have been neglecting it in their relationship. Take turns being blindfolded and then gently explore each other's bodies – this can help reconnect you. Or blindfolds can be used for super sexy fun. Why not blindfold your partner and then tease them with feathering or other touching techniques. Blindfolds definitely give another edge to bondage and domination-play.

Take this idea a bit further and wear a mask for bondage play – definitely not a frightening one! Your partner won't think it's sexy if you jump out of the wardrobe with a gimp mask on. Instead think of the exotic masks like those at the Venice Carnival or fetish-type masks.

The dominant partner can mask their face for a raunchy role-play – something like playing the captor of the innocent maiden can be sexy rather than frightening. You add a sense of mystery to your role-play and it's easier for the partner who isn't masked to fantasise about being ravished by a stranger.

Academy warning: It must be stressed that if you're ever going to gag a partner for a role-play you should exercise complete caution so that a gag doesn't slip and cause choking.

Captive clitoris
If she has let go of her inhibitions, this can be exciting for her. Handcuff her with her legs apart and each ankle tied so that she's spreadeagled on the bed. After giving her some sensual massage on her pelvis, hips, inner thighs and pubic mound with lashings of lubricant, carefully begin a gentle pulling-up of her clitoral hood. Do this gently and rhythmically. He can also gently circle and touch her clitoris, and even blow gently across it. Finally, with some tongue and lip action he can bring her to climax.

Lesson 6: A bit more S&M

Here are a few S&M-lite techniques to try. Many joke 'It hurts so good!' and actually mean it, relishing a bit of pain. Historically practices like self-flagellation during religious festivities brought people into a state of religious ecstasy. For some this undoubtedly translated into sexual ecstasy.

Let's begin with the verbal part of S&M. Think of the film *The Secretary* and how some people are turned on by being ordered to do something. A classic fantasy role-play is for the 'boss' to be unhappy with the 'secretary's' work. He commands her to come over to his desk and bend over. Next he threatens to punish her. Whether or not this threat is carried out and he spanks her bottom is one thing – but it's the dominating and even sadistic manner in which he speaks to her that might turn her on.

As long as both partners find such role-play a turn-on – and enjoy being humiliated – they can swap between roles or stick to their preferred roles.

Let's get physical

What happens when such things move into the physical? Spanking and whipping are probably the most popular S&M activities and you can buy spanking paddles and whips in any decent adult shop. Spanking and whipping increase the blood flow to the skin and can actually increase a person's ability to orgasm. This is because increasing blood flow to an area heightens the sensations there. Add some dirty talk and you've got some basic S&M.

The dominant partner can use their hand or many other implements for spanking. Even a simple wooden spoon or hairbrush can do the trick as well as a spanking paddle, though some of the shop-bought paddles have an optional fur-lined side for a gentler action.

Likewise, whips can range from the very 'vanilla' styles to barbed ones guaranteed to draw blood. That dressing-gown sash you used to tie your partner up with can also be used to whip them gently – a quick and light wrist action works.

You don't have to be into S&M to find a quick, well-delivered smack on the bottom or thighs during sex can set passion alight.

Academy rule no. 31: Never, ever smack your partner's buttocks unexpectedly. First off they might hate the sensation and second they might respond by smacking you back.

If you or your partner object to something like spanking, an alternative pain sensation is to pinch them. Light and quick pinches delivered along the buttocks or inner thighs can intensify their pleasure. If done just as your partner reaches orgasm it can heighten the pain/pleasure threshold.

Exploring different pain/pleasure sensations in this way can feel safe with a trusting partner. You know you don't really want to hurt each other – you simply want to give new and different sensations. These 'vanilla' techniques – despite seeming ridiculous to someone fully into S&M – can be exciting and titillating for many couples.

Academy warning: If you end up finding you enjoy spanking/whipping you should frequently change locations, say from the buttocks to the thighs. Fleshy areas can end up permanently damaged by repeated spankings, etc. The skin can end up with broken veins and mottling, which is not very attractive. If the skin becomes pink, move to another area of the buttocks. Remember most bruising doesn't come up for a while, so stop before you see the bruising.

Academy note: Typical S&M jargon describes the partner who does the whipping/spanking as the 'top' or 'dom', and the receiver as the 'bottom' or 'sub'. 'Dom' obviously stands for dominant and 'sub' for submissive. If you two are simply having a little fun with this then why not alternate between these two roles?

Super sexy spanking

Any Academy student who enjoys a little spanking and a bit of anal-play can try this technique. Have your partner who's being spanked lie across your lap or kneel beside them as they lie across the end of the bed. Use plenty of lubricant so that the spanking action slips and slides. If you're spanking them with your left hand, that frees up your right hand. Wear a barrier on your finger (a condom or latex glove) on your right hand so you can either finger their sphincter or rhythmically slide your finger in and out of their bottom in between spanks. That's a whole lot of stimulation.

You only need to insert your finger in and out an inch or so as you spank them. By either alternating these sensations or, if skilful, doing these in synchrony they get an amazing build-up of sexual tension.

This is the perfect time to add in sub/dom fantasy-chat. Allow yourselves to get carried away – the dom can say the things they imagine a dominatrix would. The sub might pretend they need some sort of 'correction'. By now students should be getting quite creative with their fantasy sex-chat.

Naughty nipple clamps

Sometimes even a little bit of sex-perimentation with the pain/pleasure border can add a new dimension to your sex-life. An easy way to experiment is with nipple clamps – both men and women can enjoy these and they're easily purchased at most adult shops or online.

They should only create as much pain as either of you want. Simply slip them on during foreplay or during penetrative sex if the sight of them arouses your partner. Some couples end up experimenting with clamps on her labia and his scrotum. This is a completely individual preference but it's certainly one way of trying some pain. As always you're warned not to leave them on too long – five or ten minutes is plenty.

Lipstick Lust

For nipple fun but without pain here's a sexy little tip where
he can get artistic. He takes her lipstick, preferably a hot pink
or deep red shade, and draws little circles around her nipples.
He should do it sensually, gently swirling the creamy lipstick
around them. Next he gently massages the lipstick around
your nipples, highlighting them. They look amazing and just
like the nipple shields strippers wear – quite sexy.

The sex slave massage

If you have enjoyed some sub/dom sex-play then take turns
giving each other a 'sex slave massage' as described in the last
Lecture Series. For these purposes really get into your role-
play – the sex slave has to completely indulge their master
or mistress.

Some like it hot

Often those who enjoy testing their pleasure/pain barrier try
using hot wax. In fact there's an erotic artist who uses hot
wax on his models. But here's a stern **Academy Warning**:
obviously hot wax can burn and you need to exercise extreme
caution! Never ever play with such things if you don't trust
your partner to be very careful. If you have thin or delicate
skin this is definitely not for you.

If you're exercising caution then try alternating wax and
ice-play to create different sensations. A good starting point
is to use birthday-cake candles – the wax drips more slowly.
Obviously only use good-quality candles and always test
droplets of the wax on the inside of your wrist to ensure it's
not too hot.

When testing how the droplets feel, start from a height of
about a metre to allow the wax to cool enough before hits the

skin. Definitely keep ice or cool wet cloths handy if you find the wax too hot. Ensure that drops of burning wax don't land on the skin or on your bedclothes, which could potentially start a fire. You have been warned!

So what do people get out of hot wax play? They like the fantasy-chat around it and the heat on their skin. People confide they like the sort of risqué – but pretend – chat along the lines of 'Can you feel the heat? It's no match for the heat of my cock!' or 'It's no match for the heat deep inside my pussy!' I think you get the drift.

Lesson 7: Sex games to keep having fun with

Moving on from the pain and pleasure arena, here are some good – not always clean – grown-up games to try. Although some are quite kinky, they're all fun. As noted earlier at the Academy, far too many people forget that sex should be fun. These games can help you lose any seriousness and find your frivolous, flirty and fun side.

I've included these sexy little 'games' in this diploma-level Lecture Series because it takes the more skilled lover to realise creative little techniques can titillate and keep things lively.

Come and get it

This little game will help you be inventive. By texting or e-mailing you control what happens that evening, Saturday afternoon, etc. Your messaging leaves your partner a trail of hints of where they'll find you. And maybe they'll find you sipping a glass of wine in a candlelit bathroom with a new waterproof sex toy – you decide. Your messages can also include requests, like could they bring a chilled bottle of wine or some ice cubes (don't forget how lovely it is when they trace an ice cube held between their lips up and down your body).

You could even spread your messages over a couple days if you don't live together. This way you build up the anticipation and sense of fun. Next time they can set up the 'come and get it' vibe.

Control yourself

This little sex game forces you to control yourselves. It's actually quite helpful if one of you is too quick when it comes to climaxing. You'll each need a piece of notepaper and you both write down something that you want 'controlled'. You both exchange your notepapers. It might be helpful to write down a codeword that goes with this. So she might write down that he can only do three thrusts on the command of her codeword, then he must stop penetration and start stimulating her with his hands or mouth. So her codeword might be 'sexy three', meaning three thrusts. Each partner must agree to what each other has written down.

You can imagine how this builds sexual tension. Obviously it's meant to be fun, so if he has a problem with premature ejaculation, don't use this game until he's developed better control.

What is it?

This is really a foreplay technique in the shape of a little game. One of you is blindfolded and lies down. The other spreads lashings of lubricant all over themselves including fingers, toes, chin, tip of nose, genitals etc. The lubed-up partner then touches the blindfolded partner on one of their erogenous zones. The blindfolded partner guesses what part of the body is touching them.

This is actually trickier for the blindfolded partner than you'd think. For instance, a lubed-up chin feels very much like a lubed-up palm of the hand. The twist is if they guess correctly they get to be touched wherever they want for as long as they want. If they're wrong they swap places and you start again with the other partner blindfolded.

I spy

Academy students will know the classic 'I spy' game, but this is something sexy. One of you starts by giving a clue that your partner has to guess. Be creative. As with I spy you give the first letter of a word. For example you might say, 'I spy with my little eye, something beginning with C.' They might guess 'cock' when actually you were thinking of 'cleavage'. Give each other permission to use all the rude slang names you know for erogenous zones. If they still can't guess what you mean, guide their hands or lips to the correct area. Then they have to caress and tease you there for some fun foreplay.

Truth or dare

Another excuse for a little sex-perimentation: set the scene with soft music and sexy lighting and cuddle up on the sofa. Write out five 'dares' on separate pieces of paper, fold them and place in a bowl. The dares should be a mix of pleasurable and naughty – or both! Dares give you opportunities to experiment, as they can be anything you want. For instance, one partner might want to try something new like anal fingering, or something raunchy like having to pee in front of the other.

Next take turns asking each other intimate questions like 'What's the sexiest fantasy you've ever had?' or 'Where's the most unusual place you've ever had sex?' If the question is something you don't want to answer then you must choose a dare out of the bowl. And so the game goes on for as long as you want.

Academy warning: If you decide to answer the truth to a question make sure it's not anything that would upset your partner.

Strip poker

This is another classic game to build sexual tension because the loser ends up bearing all. If you're not poker fans you can do this with any game you like. With each turn when someone loses they have to forfeit an item of clothing. No cheating allowed and you both have to abide by the rules! It can be a great technique for boosting confidence for a partner who feels a bit inhibited – once they've been playfully forced to strip slowly they'll see it's not so bad.

At the point where at least one of you is completely naked, bring out the sex toys. The next time someone loses they are teased with a sex toy for a few minutes.

X marks the spot

This is one to try when you've had a drink or two and you're ready for a laugh. Take a lipstick and mark an X on each of your favourite erogenous zones. Then your partner needs to move up your body kissing and stimulating each X in turn. This is one to take turns with.

Musical caresses

This will get you both feeling horny. To play fair, toss a die to see who gets to be in control of the music – the highest number wins the toss. Keep the CD player remote control to hand. When the music is playing, you can dive in for some foreplay or oral sex. But at any point the person in control can turn off the music and you both have to stop touching each other.

The partner with the control can tease the one who doesn't

have it – because just as they're having lots of fun with fore-play the music gets turned off. Use your power and get into a 'dom' fantasy role: say that if they do X, Y or Z to you, you'll let the music play on until you're both satisfied.

Musical positions

Another musical theme but this time you get in bed and are allowed to stay in one sex position for as long as the music is playing. This is a tough one! When the music stops he must withdraw, and when it starts again you both must get into a new position.

You might want to refresh your memory from the sex position lessons in Lecture Series 4. Even if you battle over who controls turning the music off and on, it's a fantastic way to ensure you try new positions rather than always staying in your favourite.

Tempting Twister

Everyone loves good old-fashioned Twister, but tonight do it wearing only your skimpiest and sexiest gear. Begin by smoth-ering each other with loads of your favourite massage oil so that you slip and slide as you play classic Twister. Definitely add in an extra twist where once in a position you have to try and touch each other in an erogenous zone or plant a naughty kiss somewhere when it's your turn. Eventually you'll collapse in a heap and leap into bed.

Forfeit

This is one for a fun and light-hearted mood. It's still quite sexy but in a spontaneous way. If you're cuddled up on the sofa with a glass of wine and find yourselves feeling a bit sexy, try this. Take turns doing sexy mimes while the other guesses what you're miming. For instance, you might mime giving oral sex. If your partner doesn't guess correctly they have to do a forfeit – maybe giving you a couple minutes of 'oral' or stripping off an item of clothing. Charades was never like this!

Sexy dice

You can buy 'lovers' dice' from adult stores already labelled with sexy suggestions instead of numbers. If you don't have these, use a pair of classic dice and give each number a reference. Together, agree a list of what the six numbers on a die represent, e.g., 1 = breasts, 2 = genitals, 3 = bottom, etc. For the other die you agree an action like 1 = kiss/nibble, 2 = a thrust, 3 = a rub, etc. All you need to do is take turns throwing the dice. The one who throws gets the action done to them. Easy endless fun!

Sexy spelling

This is best played when feeling relaxed, perhaps if you're already enjoying a little foreplay. Moisten your fingertip with some lubricant or use your moist tongue and write a sexy message on your lover's body. They then guess what you've written. When they guess correctly you have to do what you've written to them.

If they can't guess it then they have to do it to you once you confess what you've written. It's time for lots of licking and lapping as you spell out those naughty words on your partner's abdomen, thighs, buttocks and breasts.

Spin the bottle

A fun twist on an old game where one of you lies down and the other spreads lubricant over your abdomen. They should use lashings of something slippery all over it. They then take a small, empty bottle, e.g., a beer bottle, and spin it on your abdomen. Wherever it ends up pointing to is where they have to indulge you with lots of kissing and licking.

Be my sex slave

Make this a sexy competition where the loser has to be the sex slave. For example, the competition can be which one of you can bear an ice-cube on their naughty bits the longest. Whoever lasts the longest is the winner and the slave must indulge any of their whims (within reason of course!) for the evening.

Knock, knock

Set the scene for this role-play sex game by deciding which one of you will be the mystery visitor who knocks on the door unexpectedly. They pretend to be a door-to-door salesperson or a nosy neighbour who wants to investigate a leak, for example. Of course you let them in and immediately sexy banter begins. For instance, the door-to-door salesperson says they have some interesting products to show you that turn out be sex toys, etc. As the double entendres flow so too does flirting and fondling – and eventually full sex.

Surprise, surprise

Go back through the Academy Lecture Series but this time randomly take turns choosing an unknown page. From that page you need to try a new 'surprise' technique. You could even blindfold yourselves before randomly flicking through. Then wherever your finger lands you both pre-agree to try it. It can be a bit of a heart-stopping moment when you hit upon some of the stronger suggestions but it's a great way to generate new sex-play.

Lesson 8: After-play

Having explained before-play to Academy students early in the Lecture Series, I'd like to end on what I call after-play. After-play is how you continue a loving, sensual vibe once you've finished enjoying a fun sex game like the ones just described or when you're both exhausted from having tried a new position or two. Or even when you've enjoyed some fore-play but haven't had full sex for one reason or another and are simply cuddling together.

This is the time for some affection and to whisper loving words to each other, or simply to hold each other. We all recognise that a number of people (often men!) want to simply roll over and go to sleep after sex. But their relationship could be enhanced by allowing even a few minutes of after-play. After sex – or even after cuddling and foreplay only – is the time when the bonding hormone oxytocin is racing around your body. Use this time to savour a few quiet moments (and really that's all after-play has to be) that can deepen your emotional intimacy.

Lecture Series 8 Sex-amination

*Circle the answer that you think is correct. Count up your number of A,
B and C answers and then check the answer key below.*

1/ What is a 'top'?

A/ It's the end of the penis.

B/ It's the partner that goes on top in a sex position.

C/ It's the dominant person in something like S&M sex-play.

2/ What is Tantric breathing?

A/ It's the heavy breathing someone does after exercise.

B/ It's the type of breathing people do in yoga.

C/ It's where a couple try and sense each other's breathing and get theirs in sync.

3/ Where's the 'million-dollar spot' located?
A/ It's located between a woman's legs.
B/ It's located between a man's legs.
C/ It's located on a man's perineum 'outside' of where his prostate gland would be.

4/ What do you need to do to have a whole body orgasm?
A/ You need to touch their whole body.
B/ You need to involve your whole body in sex-play.
C/ You need to do the reverse of what you normally do when getting sexually excited.

5/ What can happen if you spank or whip the same area for too long?
A/ Your partner will get upset with you.
B/ Your partner might get bruised.
C/ The area can become bruised and end up with broken veins and mottled skin.

6/ How can wearing a blindfold improve sex?
A/ If you're not happy with your partner you don't have to see them.
B/ You can pretend you're anywhere.
C/ Taking away the sense of sight heightens your other senses.

7/ What are you supposed to do when you play sexy 'knock, knock'?
A/ Answer the door.
B/ Let your partner in and flirt with them.
C/ Use it as an opportunity for sexy role-plays and more.

8/ Why would you have a codeword when you do something like tying your partner up or role-playing?

A/ To confuse them.

B/ To make it like a secret agent fantasy.

C/ So that you can really tell when one of you wants to finish the sex game.

9/ What is after-play?

A/ It's when the team's exhausted after they play a match.

B/ It's after you've got sexually excited.

C/ It can be a few quiet moments after sex, foreplay or affection where you allow your bond to deepen or quietly enjoy the moment.

10/ What are some important things to do during anal sex?

A/ Make sure you're not smelly down there.

B/ Make sure both of you want to try it.

C/ Always use safer sex practices and lots of lubrication.

Number of As: _____

Number of Bs: _____

Number of Cs: _____

❖ Mainly As: Not acceptable

You've come all this way and you're still not paying attention. I sincerely hope you pay more attention to your partner in bed than you have in this Lecture Series. Consider returning to the beginning of these lectures.

❖ Mainly Bs: Best do better next time

Hopefully you have gained enough knowledge from the Academy to pleasure your partners in future. But do be a bit more attentive to make the most of your sex life.

❍ **Mainly Cs: Completely hot**

You're a star pupil and the Academy will be sad to see you move on to greater things.

Finally, it's goodbye from the Sex Academy and from me, your Professor of Pleasure. I hope you'll take many good memories with you as you forge new and better sexual relationships in the outside world.

There are so many important lessons to take with you. Build your confidence – both sexual and general – so that you never feel pressured to do something you don't want to. This will help you feel happy about getting what you'd like from a sexual relationship. And put your new communication skills to excellent use and discover what your partner likes and needs to enjoy sex with you. These two fundamental lessons will help you enjoy experimenting with some of the hundreds of suggestions in _Sex Academy_.

Good luck, enjoy yourself and happy loving, Dr Pam xxx

Helpful Contact Details

British Pregnancy Advisory Service: 08457 304030
Sexual Health Direct helpline: 0845 310 1334
The Gender Trust, for help with gender issues: 01273 234024
The Institute of Psychosexual Medicine, for help with issues
of sexuality and gender: 020 7580 0631
Relate, for relationship help: relate.org.uk
Sexaholics Anonymous information line: 07000 725463
Sex Wise, for confidential advice: 0800 282930

Websites

Here is a selection of adult websites. Most of these are straightforward sites selling a range of sex toys and products. **It is
your responsibility to ensure that at the time of usage any
website is secure.**

All websites are prefixed with www.

Adameve.com   Blissbox.com
Agentprovocateur.com   Blushingbuyer.co.uk
Angelicweapons.co.uk   Cherrybliss.com
Annsummers.com   Cliterati.co.uk
Athenafem.co.uk   Coco-de-mer.co.uk
Bedroompleasures.co.uk   Condomania.co.uk

Couplebox.com (to store your private pictures securely)

Curiosa.co.uk

Doublydiscreet.com

Dreamgirldirect.co.uk

Elegantlywaisted.co.uk

Emotionalbliss.com

Eroticprints.org

Erotica-readers.co.uk

Eternalspirits.com

Femmefun.com

Femininezone.com (for info and advice)

Fetteredpleasures.com

Flirtyordirty.co.uk

Getmepleasure.co.uk

Glamorousamorous.com

Goodvibes.com

Highestheaven.co.uk

Hunkystrippers.com

Idlube.co.uk (lubricants)

Lovehoney.co.uk

Male101.com (about men and sex)

Mencorp.com (strippers)

Menforalloccasions.com (escorts)

Mr-s-leather-fetters.com

Myla.com

Natcontoursuk@aol.com

No-angel.com

Passion8.com (erotica)

Pelvictomer.co.uk

Pillowtalk.co.uk

Sda.uk.net (Sexual Dysfunction Association)

Sexchampionships.com (sex game to play online)

Serpentstail.com (for hot reading)

Sexplained.com (info on STIs, etc.)

Sexshop365.co.uk

Sextoys.co.uk

Sh-womenstore.com

Shesaidboutique.com

Skintwo.com

Slapdat.co.uk (butt-slapping fun site)

Slashfic.co.uk (favourite characters in hot scenes)

Takemetobed.co.uk (erotica and porn)

Thesexystore.co.uk

Thespark.com

Wickedlywildwomen.com

Willyworries.com

Whysleep.co.uk